# JOURNEYS

# Standards-Based Assessment Resource

## Grade 5

**Houghton
Mifflin
Harcourt**

# Contents

# Overview

## Assessments and Performance Tasks

As you use the Houghton Mifflin Harcourt *Journeys* instructional program, you have a rich array of materials to foster students' achievement week by week and unit by unit. The *Standards-Based Assessment Resource* includes Assessments and Performance Tasks that align with the content in *Journeys* and give students practice with the high-stakes tests they will encounter. Rigorous tasks and questions, complex text, and technology-enhanced item formats (online only) prepare students for success on standards-based assessments. At the end of each unit, you can use an Assessment or Performance Task to obtain a broader picture of achievement.

## Assessments

The Assessments can be given three times a year, at the end of Units 1, 3, and 5. These tests are cumulative. The Unit 1 Assessment draws from Unit 1, while the Units 3 and 5 Assessments draw upon skills that have been taught in the current and previous units. The item types and assessment formats presented are the same that students will encounter on high-stakes tests and provide essential practice in test-taking strategies.

Each Assessment has four sections. The Reading section assesses comprehension and vocabulary strategies. The Writing section draws upon the grammar, spelling, and writing skills taught to date. The Listening section presents audio or read-aloud passages that assess the listening skills that students will encounter on high-stakes tests. The Research section assesses a combination of comprehension, research/media literacy, and writing skills.

The Listening section of the Assessments includes a source that students must listen to and then answer questions about. The source will not be available as text to students. If you administer a paper-and-pencil version of the Assessments, you will read the source aloud to students. If you administer the online Assessment, students will need to access audio on a computer.

# Performance Tasks

The Performance Tasks can also be given three times a year, at the end of Units 2, 4, and 6. Each Performance Task draws upon the reading, writing, and research skills taught in the current and previous units. These tasks encourage students to integrate knowledge and skills to conduct complex analysis and research.

A brief Classroom Activity will be conducted prior to each Performance Task to orient students to the context of the task. The Classroom Activity includes a summary of one source from the Performance Task and prompts for a classroom discussion. At the end of the Classroom Activity, the teacher will be directed to make a brief statement that explains the purpose of the activity within the context of the Performance Task as a whole.

Each Performance Task features two parts. Part 1 introduces a group of related text sources. Students should be encouraged to take notes as they read the sources. After the sources, students will encounter a set of questions related to the passage. The answers to the items will be scored. Part 2 introduces the essay prompt, along with a brief description of the scoring criteria. The essay will be scored using one of three rubrics.

# General Guidelines for Administering

The Assessments and Performance Tasks are group-administered and may be taken online or as a paper-and-pencil version. At Kindergarten and Grade 1, some sections of the tests are read aloud. These sections are noted in the specific guidelines for administering the tests. At Grade 2 and beyond, students can read the directions and take the tests independently. At all grades, the Listening section of the Assessments and the Classroom Activity of the Performance Tasks will be administered by the teacher.

## Test Time

The Assessments are not timed. The Performance Tasks have suggested completion times listed on the teacher overview pages.

## Allowable Resources

Students may access several resources while they complete the Assessments and Performance Tasks.

> **Pen/pencil/highlighter and blank/lined paper:** Students are encouraged to take notes throughout the Performance Tasks, and they may choose to take notes as they complete the Assessments.

> **Hard-copy dictionary:** Students are allowed to access dictionaries as they write the essay during Part 2 of the Performance Task.

> **Headphones:** All students will need headphones to complete the Listening section of each online Assessment.

## Item Types

The Assessments and the Performance Tasks include the following item types:

- Selected-response items: These multiple-choice items require students to choose an answer from several provided options. Some items will require students to select multiple correct options.

- Constructed-response items: These items require students to write or type a response.

- Interactive items: Interactive items require students to complete a table or underline a portion of the text. Interactive items online require students to interact with the text by clicking cells in a table or highlighting a portion of text.

# Guidelines for Administering Assessment 1

Use the following directions as you administer each section.

## Reading, Writing, and Research

Students will read the passages and stimuli independently, and then they will complete the corresponding items.

## Listening

The Listening prompts are below for read-aloud presentation.

**Say:** *Listen to the presentation. Then answer the questions about the presentation.*

### *Tempest over Tea Parties*

*When the British passed a new Tea Act in 1773, the colonists were as mad as hornets. Their response surprised British officials. It wasn't even a new tax. The Tea Act was just a temporary plan to benefit a British company. But the tea tax had become a symbol of the colonists' resistance.*

*People in many seaport cities stopped British ships from unloading. The most famous incident occurred in Boston. It became known as the Boston Tea Party. In December 1773, three tea ships carrying 342 chests of tea were anchored in Boston Harbor. The colonists wanted the ships to sail back to London. When the British refused, more than one hundred men took action.*

*The men boarded the ships at night, wearing blankets and face paint to look like Mohawk Indians. "In about three hours from the time we went on board, we had thus broken and thrown overboard every tea chest to be found on the ship," George Hewes recalled years later.*

**Say:** *Listen to the presentation. Then answer the questions about the presentation.*

## The Tea Boycotts

*British officials were furious about the Boston Tea Party. Colonists refused to pay the cost of the tea. This caused the British to impose new laws. The colonists again reacted angrily, but now groups of women organized boycotts.*

*The women promised to stop buying and drinking all tea, even smuggled tea. Instead, they served "liberty tea." Creative cooks boiled up many local plants to make tea substitutes. Some borrowed an American Indian recipe using mint and lemon balm.*

*Then in October 1774, more than fifty venturesome women in Edenton, North Carolina, signed a public political declaration. It stated their determined support for the colonial assembly's boycott of British tea. "We, the Ladys of Edenton, do hereby solemnly engage not to conform to the deadly Custom of Drinking Tea."*

*The Edenton declaration shocked the British. Women were not expected to get involved in politics! But in America, many people admired the Edenton women. It was a sign of the new and important role that women were playing in patriotic protests.*

**Say:** *Listen to the presentation. Then answer the questions about the presentation.*

## James Otis

*In 1761, James Otis, a young Massachusetts lawyer, challenged a British law. The law gave customs officers the right to search colonists' homes for smuggled goods. In a five-hour speech, Otis argued that this was a violation of the colonists' rights. It was during his speech that Otis said his famous words, "Taxation without representation is tyranny!" Otis believed that the British did not have the right to tax the colonists. The British government did not represent them.*

*Young John Adams, future president of the United States, was at the court that day. He would name this moment as the first act of resistance to oppressive British policies. Although Otis lost the case, the British did not want to make the public angry by enforcing the law. In later years, Otis played a major role in pushing for the interests of the American colonists. He spoke out against many British policies. He helped plant the seeds for the American Revolution.*

# Guidelines for Administering Performance Task 1

## Space Exploration

**Classroom Activity** *(20 minutes)*

1.  Allow students to independently read "Apollo, To The Moon!" This article focuses on President Kennedy issuing a challenge to the country to have a man on the moon by the end of the 1960s. It explains his reasons for posing this challenge and the steps that NASA took to get there.

2.  Lead a brief class discussion about the article, using the questions below.

    **Question 1:** Why did NASA begin the Apollo project? How do key details in the article help explain this main idea?

    **Question 2:** What are some reasons that space exploration is important to the United States?

3.  Explain that students will use this article and two other articles to write a story about space exploration for other students and teachers.

## Student Task Overview

**Part 1** *(55 minutes)*

Students will examine the additional stimuli independently and will take notes. They will then respond to constructed-response and selected-response items.

**Part 2** *(45 minutes)*

Students will continue to have access to the sources they utilized in the Classroom Activity and Part 1. They will refer to their notes and their answers to the items to write a narrative. They will prewrite, draft, and revise that narrative. The narrative created at the end of Part 2 will be scored. Reading notes from Part 1 and prewriting and drafting from Part 2 will not be scored.

## Task Specifications and Scoring Rubrics

Review the REMEMBER section at the end of the student performance task to remind students about the elements of a well-written narrative.

Score student responses using the Performance Task: Narrative Writing Rubric.

# Guidelines for Administering Assessment 2

Use the following directions as you administer each section.

## Reading, Writing, and Research

Students will read the texts and stimuli independently complete the corresponding items.

## Listening

The Listening prompts are below for read-aloud presentation.

**Say:** *Listen to the presentation. Then answer the questions about the presentation.*

### Cougars in North America

*When people think of big cats, they often think of the lions that rule the African plains or the tigers that live in the jungles of Asia. But North America is home to its own big cat: the cougar.*

*Scientists who study cougars have determined three things that these creatures need in their habitats. They need food, places to hide, and a lot of space.*

*Cougars need places to hide to stalk their prey. The thick layer of plants and bushes on a forest floor allows good cover for a cougar as it crouches low to follow a deer. A hilly, rocky terrain can also provide many hiding places for cougars.*

*Cougars also need a lot of space. Every cougar has a home range, the area of land where it hunts and lives. One male cougar's territory can be anywhere from 25 to 500 square miles.*

*The cougar's future in North America is uncertain. If cougars in North America are to survive, they will need people to help them.*

**Say:** *Listen to the presentation. Then answer the questions about the presentation.*

## Water Buffalo

*Water buffalo are native to India, China, and other parts of Asia. They can grow to be six feet tall at the shoulder. Some water buffalo can weigh as much as 3,200 pounds. Because they are large and strong, water buffalo have been used as domesticated work animals for thousands of years.*

*There are two main types of domesticated water buffalo: the swamp buffalo and the river buffalo. In southern China and other regions where rice is an important crop, domesticated swamp buffalos pull plows and carry heavy loads. Their enormous horns sweep back toward their shoulders. Swamp buffalo are rarely milked. When their age or an injury keeps them from working in the fields, they may be used for food.*

*River buffalo are domesticated dairy animals. They are an important source of milk in countries such as India, Pakistan, and Egypt. People in these areas often cook with ghee, a kind of butter made from river buffalo milk. River buffalos' horns droop or curl by the sides of their heads.*

**Say:** *Listen to the presentation. Then answer the questions about the presentation.*

## Brainy Bottlenoses

*Bottlenose dolphins are the best-known species of dolphins. Bottlenose dolphins are the dolphins people see most often in marine shows. These well-trained animals certainly seem intelligent, but what do scientific studies show?*

*Because language is a sign of intelligence, scientists have long been interested in dolphin communication. Dolphins produce clicks, squeaks, and whistles. The sounds help them navigate through dark waters and hunt for food. Do the dolphins also use the sounds as a kind of language?*

*It is unlikely that dolphins' sounds have meaning in the same way that human words and sentences have meaning. But studies of one bottle-nose dolphin showed that these animals have the ability to understand language concepts. With a sign-language vocabulary of about forty words and learned rules about word order, the dolphin could distinguish the meanings of thousands of sentences. The ability to learn complex commands is a sign of brainpower. These social animals surely put it to use in the wild.*

# Guidelines for Administering Performance Task 2

## Life in the Old West

### Classroom Activity *(20 minutes)*

1. Allow students to independently read "Gold!" This article focuses on the California Gold Rush of 1848. The article describes how thousands of prospectors traveled for hundreds or even thousands of miles in hopes of making a quick fortune.

2. Lead a brief class discussion about the article using the questions below.

   **Question 1:** How did the discovery of gold in California change the lives of many Americans? How do key details in the text explain this main idea?

   **Question 2:** In what ways did the promise of easily found gold outweigh the dangers miners faced?

3. Explain that students will use this article and two other articles to write an opinion essay about life in the Old West for other students and teachers.

## Student Task Overview

### Part 1 *(55 minutes)*

Students will examine the additional stimuli independently and will take notes. They will then respond to constructed-response and selected-response items.

### Part 2 *(45 minutes)*

Students will continue to have access to the sources they used in the Classroom Activity and Part 1. They will refer to their notes and their answers to the items to write an opinion paper. They will prewrite, draft, and revise that report. The report created at the end of Part 2 will be scored. Reading notes in Part 1 and prewriting and drafting in Part 2 will not be scored.

## Task Specifications and Scoring Rubrics

Review the REMEMBER section at the end of the student performance task to remind students about the elements of a well-written opinion essay.

Score student responses using the Performance Task: Opinion Writing Rubric.

# Guidelines for Administering Assessment 3

Use the following directions as you administer each section.

## Reading, Writing, and Research

Students will read the articles and stimuli independently, and then they will complete the corresponding items.

## Listening

The Listening prompts are below for read-aloud presentation.

**Say:** *Listen to the presentation. Then answer questions about the presentation.*

### Saving Leo

*Snow leopards live in the frigid high mountains and plateaus of Central Asia. In Pakistan, they are critically endangered; fewer than three hundred remain. That is why a goat herder was surprised to come upon a snow leopard cub one day in 2005. The cub was tiny, just a few weeks old. It was an orphan, and the herder knew it needed help. He took it home.*

*After the herder got in touch with the World Wildlife Fund, the little snow leopard came to live with a specialist named Kamal-ud-din. Kamal cared for the cub, naming him Leo.*

*Leo became famous in Pakistan, where people hoped that he would find a suitable home. It was not possible to return Leo to the wild. A snow leopard cannot survive without the training it receives from its mother.*

*Pakistan had no wildlife centers where Leo could live, so officials contacted the Wildlife Conservation Society, which runs the Bronx Zoo in New York City. After a farewell ceremony in Islamabad, Leo traveled by plane to the United States to his new home in the Himalayan Highlands exhibit at the Bronx Zoo, where he now thrives.*

**Say:** *Listen to the presentation. Then answer questions about the presentation.*

### Nellie Bly, Star Reporter

*In the 1800s, most people, especially men, thought that newspaper work was not fit for women. But Nellie Bly broke the rules and made her mark as a fearless reporter who took on many dangerous assignments.*

*Surprisingly, a letter to a newspaper editor started Bly's career. In 1880, a columnist for the* Pittsburgh Dispatch *wrote that women should stay home to cook, clean, and sew. While this view was not uncommon at the time, it outraged young Elizabeth Cochrane. She fired off a letter saying that many women had no choice but to work.*

*The paper's editor loved the letter; when he met Elizabeth, he hired her on the spot.*

*The paper wanted her to write about cooking and fashion, but she preferred to write about topics such as child labor and poverty under the pen name Nellie Bly. When she moved to New York City to look for reporting jobs, she faced the same challenges.*

*Finally, an editor presented her with a risky dare: would she pretend to be ill and go undercover at a mental hospital? Bly took on the challenge and wrote about her experiences during her stay there. Her investigation led to improved conditions at the asylum and made her one of the first investigative reporters.*

**Say:** *Listen to the presentation. Then answer the questions about the presentation.*

## Help for Threatened Otters

*Scientists estimate that more than fifteen thousand sea otters once lived off the coast of California. California sea otters were listed as a threatened species in 1977. What caused their numbers to drop?*

*The dense fur of sea otters keeps the animals warm as they swim in cold Pacific waters. But this fur also attracted hunters. Only about one hundred otters were left in California waters by the early 1900s. Efforts began to protect otters' breeding grounds and to ban hunting.*

*Unlike other marine mammals, sea otters do not have a layer of fat to keep them warm. If their fur gets coated with oil, they can die from the cold. Because oil may spill from ships or tankers, people are trying to move shipping routes away from otter habitats.*

*Otters can also drown when they get caught in fishing nets. They may get diseases from the sea urchins, crabs, and other animals that they eat. Their limited food supply may also contain poisons from pollution.*

*Otter populations may not be in as much danger as they were in the early 1900s, but they still face many dangerous threats.*

# Guidelines for Administering Performance Task 3

## Everglades National Park

### Classroom Activity *(20 minutes)*

1. Allow students to independently read "Alligators and the Everglades." This article from a wildlife magazine focuses on the impact the American alligator has on the ecosystem of the Everglades. The article describes how the alligators' hole-digging behavior provides homes, water, and food for other animals during the Everglades' dry season.

2. Lead a brief class discussion about the article, using the questions below.

   **Question 1:** How does the alligator help other animals survive the dry season in the Everglades?

   **Question 2:** Why isn't the alligator dangerous to those animals during the dry season?

3. Explain that students will use this magazine article and two other articles to write a report about Everglades National Park for others to read.

## Student Task Overview

### Part 1 *(55 minutes)*

Students will examine the additional stimuli independently and will take notes. They will then respond to constructed-response and selected-response items.

### Part 2 *(45 minutes)*

Students will continue to have access to the sources they used in the Classroom Activity and Part 1. They will refer to their notes and answers to the items in Part 1 to write a report. They will prewrite, draft, and revise that report. The report created at the end of Part 2 will be scored. Reading notes from Part 1 and prewriting and drafting from Part 2 will not be scored.

## Task Specifications and Scoring Rubrics

Review the REMEMBER section at the end of the student performance task to remind students about the elements of a well-written informative essay.

Score student responses using the Performance Task: Informative/Explanatory Writing Rubric.

# Scoring and Interpreting the Results

## Scoring

The answers to the Assessments and Performance Tasks can be found in the Answer Keys section. Each correct response to a selected-response item is worth one point. Each constructed-response item is worth two points. Constructed-response items and essay responses should be scored using the rubrics provided in this book. Sample answers to the constructed-response items are given on the Answer Key and should be used as a guide to score a student's responses. Because these questions require students to think deeply about comprehension, both the teacher and students can learn a great deal by discussing students' responses and their reasoning.

Duplicate a Test Record Form for each student and enter the scores in the Student Score column. This form will allow you to track a student's performance across the year. If you require a percentage score for each test to help in assigning grades, apply the formula in the optional Final Score row and record that score.

## Interpreting

Consider each student's scores on the Test Record Form. Students who achieve an Acceptable Score (indicated on the form) or higher are most likely ready to move to the next unit in the book.

For struggling students, duplicate the Answer Key. Circle the item numbers answered incorrectly for each Assessment or Performance Task and compare the corresponding skills indicated. Look for patterns among the errors to help you decide which skills need reteaching and more practice.

# Assessment 1

| Item Number | Correct Answer | Unit, Lesson, Program Skill | CCSS | Depth of Knowledge |
|---|---|---|---|---|
| | | **READING** | | |
| 1 | C; D | U1L3: Comprehension: Idioms | L.5.5b | 3 |
| 2 | B | U1L1: Comprehension: Point of View | RL.5.6 | 2 |
| 3 | B | U1L3: Comprehension: Compare and Contrast | RL.5.3 | 3 |
| 4 | disbelief | U1L2: Vocabulary Strategy: Prefixes *non-*, *un-*, *dis-*, *mis-* | L.5.4b | 2 |
| 5 | See rubric on p. T24. | U1L2: Comprehension: Characterization | RL.5.3 | 3 |
| | Sample two-point response: Rick's feelings have changed from him being very focused on the science fair to back to being his easygoing, funny self. His best friend's feelings have changed from being frustrated because his friend was acting so serious and was preoccupied with the science fair, to happy to have his "old friend" back! | | | |
| | Sample one-point response: Rick went from serious to funny. His best friend went from frustrated to happy. | | | |
| 6 | B, E | U1L4: Comprehension: Sequence of Events | RI.5.1 | 2 |
| 7 | B | U1L1: Vocabulary Strategy: Using Context | L.5.4a | 2 |
| 8 | B | U1L4: Vocabulary Strategy: Suffixes *-ion, -tion* | L.5.4b | 3 |
| 9 | A, D | U1L3: Comprehension: Idioms | L.5.5b | 3 |
| 10 | B | U1L2: Vocabulary Strategy: Prefixes *non-*, *un-*, *dis-*, *mis-* | L.5.4b | 3 |
| 11 | C | U1L4: Comprehension: Narrative Pacing | RI.5.1 | 3 |
| 12 | 1, 2, 5, 4, 3 | U1L4: Comprehension: Sequence of Events | RI.5.1 | 3 |
| 13 | C | U1L4: Comprehension: Narrative Pacing | RI.5.1 | 2 |
| 14 | See rubric on p. T24. | U1L4: Comprehension: Narrative Pacing | RI.5.1 | 4 |
| | Sample two-point response: The main problem in both articles is a smaller American military needing to overcome a larger British military. In "Valley Forge" the article is told as a series of events that happened. In "Father of The American Navy" the article is told more like a story with a lot of action and dialogue. Both articles have a main character that is a hero that helps lead the American military to victory. | | | |
| | Sample one-point response: Both have the same problem of needing to overcome the British military. Both articles have a main character that is a hero that helps lead the American military to victory. | | | |
| 15 | D | U1L3: Comprehension: Formal and Informal Language | L.5.3b | 1 |
| 16 | A | U1L5: Vocabulary Strategy: Suffixes *-ly, -ful* | L.5.4b | 2 |
| 17 | A; "Miss Lydia joined Dad and me..." | U1L1: Comprehension: Point of View | RL.5.6 | 3 |
| 18 | C | U1L5: Comprehension: Theme | RL.5.2 | 2 |
| 19 | B, D | U1L3: Vocabulary Strategy: Using Context | L.5.4a | 3 |
| 20 | "Dad got a distant..." | U1L2: Comprehension: Theme | RL.5.2 | 2 |

| Item Number | Correct Answer | Unit, Lesson, Program Skill | CCSS | Depth of Knowledge |
|---|---|---|---|---|
| | | **WRITING** | | |
| 21 | grete | U1L2: Spelling: Long *a* and Long *e* | L.5.2e | 1 |
| 22 | A | U1L3: Spelling: Long *i* and Long *o* | L.5.2e | 1 |
| 23 | B | U1L1: Grammar: Complete Sentences | W.5.5 | 2 |
| 24 | B | U1L2: Grammar: Kinds of Sentences | W.5.5 | 1 |
| 25 | D | U1L4: Grammar: Common and Proper Nouns | W.5.5 | 2 |
| 26 | B, C, E | U1L3: Writing: Elaboration | W.5.3d | 2 |
| 27 | shake, shiver | U1L3: Writing: Elaboration | W.5.3d | 2 |
| 28 | C | U1L3: Writing: Elaboration | W.5.3d | 2 |
| 29 | C | U1L3: Writing: Elaboration | W.5.3d | 2 |
| 30 | See rubric on p. T24. | U1L3: Writing: Elaboration | W.5.3d | 3 |

Sample two-point response: We have a family tradition that I look forward to with great excitement and anticipation. When my grandparents go on a vacation, they take me along for a fascinating time. We always visit at least one museum or research site. This year, we visited a museum of art about the Wild West. My friend Joey said, "That sounds almost painfully dull." I know you, too, would say it was uneventful and boring, but we saw historical paintings of cowboys wearing brightly colored cloths around their necks. They wore dusty boots and hats with wide brims. Some of the cowboys were shown at camp or riding horses and roping cattle. The paintings were very colorful. I enjoyed my visit!

Sample one-point response: We have a family tradition. When my grandparents go on a vacation, they take me along for a fascinating time. We always visit at least one museum or research site. This year, we visited a museum of art. My friend Joey said, "That sounds almost painfully dull." I know you, too, would say it was uneventful, but we saw paintings that depicted the history of the Wild West. Some of the paintings showed cowboys riding horses. Some cowboys were shown roping cattle. I enjoyed the paintings very much.

| Item Number | Correct Answer | Unit, Lesson, Program Skill | CCSS | Depth of Knowledge |
|---|---|---|---|---|
| | | **LISTENING** | | |
| 31 | C | U1L2: Speaking and Listening: Draw and Support Conclusions | SL.5.3 | 1 |
| 32 | A, C | U1L2: Speaking and Listening: Draw and Support Conclusions | SL.5.3 | 2 |
| 33 | D; D | U1L2: Speaking and Listening: Draw and Support Conclusions | SL.5.3 | 3 |
| 34 | A | U1L2: Speaking and Listening: Draw and Support Conclusions | SL.5.3 | 2 |
| 35 | D | U1L2: Speaking and Listening: Draw and Support Conclusions | SL.5.3 | 1 |
| 36 | B; D | U1L2: Speaking and Listening: Draw and Support Conclusions | SL.5.3 | 3 |
| 37 | B, E | U1L2: Speaking and Listening: Draw and Support Conclusions | SL.5.3 | 3 |
| 38 | A | U1L2: Speaking and Listening: Draw and Support Conclusions | SL.5.3 | 2 |
| 39 | C | U1L2: Speaking and Listening: Draw and Support Conclusions | SL.5.3 | 1 |
| | | **RESEARCH** | | |
| 40 | B | U1L1: Research and Media Literacy: Analyze Sources | W.5.8 | 2 |
| 41 | B, F | U1L1: Research and Media Literacy: Analyze Sources | W.5.8 | 2 |

| Item Number | Correct Answer | Unit, Lesson, Program Skill | CCSS | Depth of Knowledge |
|---|---|---|---|---|
| 42 | C, E | U1L1: Research and Media Literacy: Analyze Sources | W.5.8 | 2 |
| 43 | "First, a root…", "Later, shoots and leaves…" | U1L4: Research and Media Literacy: Interpret Information from Visual Source | RI.5.7 | 2 |
| 44 | " The action reaches a …" " The parts of the …" | U1L4: Research and Media Literacy: Interpret Information from Visual Source | RI.5.1 | 2 |

# Performance Task 1

| Item Number | Correct Answer | Unit, Lesson, Program Skill | CCSS | Depth of Knowledge |
|---|---|---|---|---|
| 1 | See rubric on p. T24. | U1L1: Research and Media Literacy: Analyze Sources | RI.5.7 | 4 |
| | Sample two-point response: President Kennedy and Mae Jemison both made a difference in the field of space exploration. Source 1 says that Kennedy spoke to Congress and led the push to explore space more than they had in the past. Source 2 states that Mae Jemison was a science mission specialist and tested the effects of weightlessness in space. | | | |
| | Sample one-point response: Mae Jemison and Buzz Aldrin helped make advances in the field of space exploration. Buzz Aldrin took the first steps on the moon, and Mae Jemison was the first African American woman to go into space. | | | |
| 2 | See rubric on p. T24. | U2L6: Research and Media Literacy: Use Evidence | RI.5.1 | 3 |
| | Sample two-point response: Source 3 would be the most helpful in understanding how astronauts traveled to space. Source 3 tells about different types of spacecraft from capsules, to modules, to shuttles. Source 3 tells the reader how each of the different missions had different spacecraft that changed through the years. | | | |
| | Sample one-point response: Source 3 would be the most helpful because it describes the different types of spacecraft the astronauts used. | | | |
| 3 | See answer below. | U2L10: Research and Media Literacy: Interpret Information from Text Source | W.5.8 | 3 |
| | Fact 1: Source 3; Fact 2: Sources 1 and 2; Fact 3: Sources 1 and 3 | | | |
| Essay Response | See rubric on p. T25. | U1L5: Writing: Narrative | W.5.3 | 4 |

# Assessment 2

| Item Number | Correct Answer | Unit, Lesson, Program Skill | CCSS | Depth of Knowledge |
|---|---|---|---|---|
| | | **READING** | | |
| 1 | C; D | U3L11: Comprehension: Cause and Effect | RL.5.5 | 3 |
| 2 | C | U2L7: Vocabulary Strategy: Adage and Proverbs | L.5.5b | 3 |
| 3 | D | U2L6: Vocabulary Strategy: Synonyms | L.5.5c | 2 |
| 4 | D | U2L7: Comprehension: Understanding Characters | RL.5.3 | 2 |
| 5 | See answer below. | U3L12: Vocabulary Strategy: Figurative Language | L.5.5a | 2 |
| | big chunks of ice broke off the ice face, sounding like thunder… | | | |
| 6 | B | U2L8: Comprehension: Author's Purpose | RI.5.8 | 3 |
| 7 | B, D, E | U2L6: Comprehension: Quotes and Description | RI.5.1 | 3 |
| 8 | See rubric on p. T24. | U2L10: Comprehension: Main Ideas and Details | RI.5.2 | 3 |
| | Sample two-point response: Humans have moved into areas where bears already live. The article says, "People have cut down trees to develop land for homes, industry, and roads." Now bears have grown used to living near humans. When searching for food, they wander near houses and will eat food left out by humans. | | | |
| | Sample one-point response: Humans live where bears used to, so bears get food left out by humans. | | | |
| 9 | B | U2L8: Vocabulary Strategy: Prefixes *en-, re-, pre-, pro-* | L.5.1 | 2 |
| 10 | See answers below. | U3L11: Comprehension: Cause and Effect | RL.5.5 | 3 |
| | Because bears are…; In times when… | | | |
| 11 | See rubric on p. T24. | U3L13: Comprehension: Conclusions and Generalizations | RI.5.1 | 2 |
| | Sample two-point response: The author suggests that if the reader meets a bear, he or she should remain calm, leave slowly, and offer the bear a way to escape. | | | |
| | Sample one-point response: If you meet a bear, don't panic. | | | |
| 12 | trusted, friendship | U3L13: Comprehension: Conclusions and Generalizations | RI.5.1 | 1 |
| 13 | B | U3L13: Comprehension: Text Structure | RI.5.3 | 2 |
| 14 | D, E | U3L15: Comprehension: Compare and Contrast | RI.5.3 | 2 |
| 15 | C | U3L14: Vocabulary Strategy: Greek and Latin Roots | L.5.4b | 2 |
| 16 | A | U2L6: Comprehension: Domain-Specific Vocabulary | L.5.6 | 3 |
| 17 | A, C | U2L7: Comprehension: Understanding Characters | RL.5.3 | 3 |
| 18 | C | U2L10: Vocabulary Strategy: Shades of Meaning | L.5.4 | 3 |
| 19 | C; A, D | U2L9: Comprehension: Conclusions and Generalizations | RL.5.1 | 3 |
| 20 | See answers below. | U2L9: Comprehension: Point of View | RL.5.6 | 4 |
| | D; He was exhausted…; They were selfish…; The traveler decided… | | | |

| Item Number | Correct Answer | Unit, Lesson, Program Skill | CCSS | Depth of Knowledge |
|---|---|---|---|---|
| WRITING | | | | |
| 21 | whistel, struggel | U3L15: Spelling: Final Schwa + /l/ Sounds | L.5.2e | 1 |
| 22 | A | U2L10: Grammar: Direct Quotations and Interjections | L.5.1a | 1 |
| 23 | A | U2L6: Spelling: Vowel + /r/ Sounds | L.5.2e | 1 |
| 24 | B | U3L12: Writing: Organization | W.5.1a | 2 |
| 25 | C | U2L7: Grammar: Direct and Indirect Objects | L.5.3a | 2 |
| 26 | faded, repair, nice | U3L11: Writing: Elaboration | W.5.1a | 2 |
| 27 | A | U2L7: Writing: Elaboration | W.5.2d | 2 |
| 28 | A | U3L12: Grammar: Verb Tenses | L.5.1d | 2 |
| 29 | C, D | U2L6: Writing: Organization | W.5.2e | 2 |
| 30 | See rubric on p. T24. | U3L11: Writing: Elaboration | W.5.1a | 3 |
| | Sample two-point response: Last year my family took the best summer vacation ever. We drove for hours to get to California to visit my funny uncle. Along the way we stopped at the Grand Canyon and hiked for many miles. We had quite an adventure! | | | |
| | Sample one-point response: Last year my family took a summer vacation. It was fun. We drove to California to visit my uncle. Along the way we stopped at the Grand Canyon and hiked. We had a great adventure! | | | |
| LISTENING | | | | |
| 31 | C | U3L12: Speaking and Listening: Identify and Interpret Purpose, Central Idea, and Key Points | SL.5.3 | 2 |
| 32 | A, B; C | U2L8: Speaking and Listening: Identify Ideas and Supporting Evidence | SL.5.3 | 1 |
| 33 | D | U2L8: Speaking and Listening: Identify Ideas and Supporting Evidence | SL.5.3 | 2 |
| 34 | B; A, D | U3L12: Speaking and Listening: Identify and Interpret Purpose, Central Idea, and Key Points | SL.5.3 | 2 |
| 35 | B, C | U2L8: Speaking and Listening: Identify Ideas and Supporting Evidence | SL.5.3 | 1 |
| 36 | D | U2L8: Speaking and Listening: Identify Ideas and Supporting Evidence | SL.5.3 | 3 |
| 37 | D | U3L12: Speaking and Listening: Identify and Interpret Purpose, Central Idea, and Key Points | SL.5.3 | 3 |
| 38 | A, B | U2L8: Speaking and Listening: Identify Ideas and Supporting Evidence | SL.5.3 | 3 |
| 39 | A | U2L8: Speaking and Listening: Identify Ideas and Supporting Evidence | SL.5.3 | 1 |

| Item Number | Correct Answer | Unit, Lesson, Program Skill | CCSS | Depth of Knowledge |
|---|---|---|---|---|
| | | **RESEARCH** | | |
| 40 | See answers below. | U2L6: Research: Use Evidence | W.5.8 | 2 |
| | However, cell phones…; Students can look…; They can even… | | | |
| 41 | See answers below. | U3L11: Research: Locate Information from a Text Source | W.5.8 | 2 |
| | Unfortunately, cell phones…; Students may use… | | | |
| 42 | D, E | U2L10: Research: Interpret Information from a Text Source | W.5.8 | 2 |
| 43 | B | U3L14: Research: Interpret Information from a Visual Source | RI.5.7 | 2 |
| 44 | C, D, E | U3L13: Research: Conclusions and Generalizations | RI.5.1 | 2 |

# Performance Task 2

| Item Number | Correct Answer | Unit, Lesson, Program Skill | CCSS | Depth of Knowledge |
|---|---|---|---|---|
| 1 | See rubric on p. T24. | U4L17: Research and Media Literacy: Use Evidence | RI.5.1 | 3 |
| | Sample two-point response: Pioneers faced many challenges as they traveled to the West. Source #3 states that pioneers had to leave their families and friends behind. Source #3 also states that many people died or were injured on the trip. This is important because it gives additional examples of ways pioneers struggled to safely reach the West. | | | |
| | Sample one-point response: Pioneers faced many challenges as they traveled to the West. Source #3 states that pioneers had to leave their families and friends behind. People also died or were injured along the way. | | | |
| 2 | See rubric on p. T24. | U3L11: Research and Media Literacy: Locate Information from Text Source | RI.5.1 | 4 |
| | Sample two-point response: Settlers faced many risks on the trip out west. Miners left behind families with only a dream of finding wealth. Settlers along the Santa Fe Trail faced attacks. Many people along the Oregon Trail were injured or died. | | | |
| | Sample one-point response: Settlers faced many risks. People who took one of the large trails out west risked death or injury. | | | |
| 3 | See answers below. | U4L19: Research and Media Literacy: Locate Information from Text Source | W.5.9 | 3 |
| | Idea 1 = sources 1, 2, 3; Idea 2 = source 1; Idea 3 = source 2; Idea 4 = source 3 | | | |
| Essay Response | See rubric on p. T27. | U3L15: Writing: Opinion | W.5.8 | 4 |

# Assessment 3

| Item Number | Correct Answer | Unit, Lesson, Program Skill | CCSS | Depth of Knowledge |
|---|---|---|---|---|
| | | **READING** | | |
| 1 | D | U5L21: Vocabulary Strategy: Shades of Meaning | L.5.4a | 3 |
| 2 | 3, 2, 1, 4, 5 | U5L21: Comprehension: Sequence of Events | RL.5.5 | 2 |
| 3 | Rosa, She, Her | U5L24: Comprehension: Point of View | RL.5.6 | 2 |
| 4 | A; D | U4L20: Comprehension: Story Structure | RL.5.5 | 3 |
| 5 | B; C | U4L19: Comprehension: Characterization | RL.5.1 | 3 |
| 6 | A | U4L20: Vocabulary Strategy: Figurative Language | L.5.5 | 3 |
| 7 | A, C, E | U5L24: Comprehension: Cause and Effect | RL.5.5 | 3 |
| 8 | C | U5L21: Comprehension: Author's Word Choice | RL.5.4 | 3 |
| 9 | See rubric p. T24. | U4L20: Comprehension: Theme | RL.5.2 | 3 |
| | Sample two-point response: Detail 1: It's strange, but afterward, I felt different. It felt like I'd suddenly gotten a little taller, or a little stronger, or a little better. <br> Detail 2: Throughout the effort, I discovered that I was becoming more outgoing. I was less fearful of speaking up or of taking charge of a situation. | | | |
| | Sample one-point response: It's strange, but afterward, I felt different. It felt like I'd suddenly gotten a little taller, or a little stronger, or a little better | | | |
| 10 | "When I thought…", "Yes, my efforts…." | U5L22: Comprehension: Theme | RL.5.2 | 2 |
| 11 | C, D, E | U4L18: Comprehension: Fact and Opinion | RI.5.8 | 2 |
| 12 | C | U5L25: Vocabulary Strategy: Analogies | L.5.5c | 3 |
| 13 | B | U4L18: Comprehension: Main Idea and Details | RI.5.2 | 2 |
| 14 | See rubric p. T24. | U5L25: Comprehension: Primary Source | RI.5.8 | 4 |
| | Sample two-point answer: Don Quixote admires all that is good and detests all that is evil. When he mistakes windmills for ferocious giants, he fights them, thinking they are evil. On the other hand, he is gentle toward women, treating them with courtesy and respect. | | | |
| | Sample one-point answer: Don Quixote attacks windmills he thinks are giants and treats women with special courtesy. | | | |
| 15 | A; C | U5L24: Vocabulary Strategy: Using Context | L.5.4a | 2 |
| 16 | A | U5L23: Vocabulary Strategy: Adages and Proverbs | L.5.5b | 2 |
| 17 | B, C, D, F | U4L18: Comprehension: Main Idea and Details | RI.5.2 | 3 |
| 18 | B | U4L18: Comprehension: Fact and Opinion | RI.5.1 | 3 |
| 19 | B | U5L25: Comprehension: Explain Historical Events | RI.5.3 | 2 |
| 20 | A | U4L18: Vocabulary Strategy: Homophones and Homographs | L.5.5c | 1 |

| Item Number | Correct Answer | Unit, Lesson, Program Skill | CCSS | Depth of Knowledge |
|---|---|---|---|---|
| **WRITING** | | | | |
| 21 | "By the time…" | U5L22: Grammar: Perfect Tenses | L.5.1b | 1 |
| 22 | arriveing | U4L16: Spelling: Words with -ed or -ing | L.5.2e | 1 |
| 23 | See rubric on p. T24. | U4L17: Writing: Elaboration | W.5.1a | 3 |
| 23 | Sample two-point answer: These forests consist of coniferous trees, including pine, hemlock, spruce, and balsam fir, as well as deciduous trees, such as aspen, birch, and maple. Wild blueberries and cranberries also grow in the forests. The forests of New Brunswick are home to several kinds of animals—white-tailed deer, moose, porcupines, raccoons, and migratory birds. Many rivers support these diverse life forms. | | | |
| 23 | Sample one-point answer: Trees like pines and aspens grow there. Animals like deer live in the forests, too. | | | |
| 24 | C | U4L19: Spelling: Suffixes: -ful, -ly, -ness, -less, -ment | L.5.2e | 1 |
| 25 | B | U4L18: Grammar: Prepositions and Prepositional Phrases | L.5.1a | 2 |
| 26 | B | U4L20: Grammar: Proper Mechanics and Writing Titles | L.5.2b | 2 |
| 27 | D | U5L22: Writing: Organization | W.5.2e | 2 |
| 28 | C | U5L23: Writing: Organization | W.5.1a | 2 |
| 29 | C, D | U5L25: Writing: Elaboration | W.5.3d | 2 |
| 30 | A | U4L17: Writing: Elaboration | W.5.1b | 2 |
| **LISTENING** | | | | |
| 31 | B | U4L16: Speaking and Listening: Draw and Support Conclusions | SL.5.3 | 1 |
| 32 | A, B | U5L23: Speaking and Listening: Identify and Interpret Purpose, Central Ideas, Key Points | SL.5.3 | 1 |
| 33 | C | U5L23: Speaking and Listening: Identify and Interpret Purpose, Central Ideas, Key Points | SL.5.2 | 2 |
| 34 | D | U5L23: Speaking and Listening: Identify and Interpret Purpose, Central Ideas, Key Points | SL.5.2 | 2 |
| 35 | B, E | U4L16: Speaking and Listening: Draw and Support Conclusions | SL.5.3 | 2 |
| 36 | D; C | U4L16: Speaking and Listening: Draw and Support Conclusions | SL.5.3 | 3 |
| 37 | C | U4L16: Speaking and Listening: Draw and Support Conclusions | SL.5.3 | 3 |
| 38 | C | U5L23: Speaking and Listening: Identify and Interpret Purpose, Central Ideas, Key Points | SL.5.3 | 3 |
| 39 | See answer below. | U5L23: Speaking and Listening: Identify and Interpret Purpose, Central Ideas, Key Points | SL.5.2 | 1 |
| 39 | Facts about Otters: eat shellfish and urchins, dense fur; Conservation Efforts: changes to shipping routes, bans on hunting and fishing, pollution control | | | |

| Item Number | Correct Answer | Unit, Lesson, Program Skill | CCSS | Depth of Knowledge |
|---|---|---|---|---|
| | | **RESEARCH** | | |
| 40 | E, F | U5L25: Research and Media Literacy: Analyze Sources | W.5.7 | 2 |
| 41 | B | U4L19: Research and Media Literacy: Locate Information from Text Source | RI.5.7 | 2 |
| 42 | B, C | U5L21: Research and Media Literacy: Interpret Information from Text Sources | W.5.8 | 2 |
| 43 | "For example, the…", "The aye-aye…" | U4L17: Research and Media Literacy: Use Evidence | W.5.8 | 2 |
| 44 | In fact, many… | U4L19: Research and Media Literacy: Locate Information from Text Source | RI.5.7 | 2 |

# Performance Task 3

| Item Number | Correct Answer | Unit, Lesson, Program Skill | CCSS | Depth of Knowledge |
|---|---|---|---|---|
| | | **SECTION HEAD** | | |
| 1 | See rubric on p. T24. | U5L21: Research and Media Literacy: Interpret Information from Text Source | W.5.8 | 3 |
| | Sample two-point response: In Source #1, the author says that alligators affect the ecosystem of the Everglades by making gator holes that provide homes, food, and water for other animals. In Source #2, the author says that the egret helps keep the number of fish in the Everglades under control. In Source #3, the author says that human activity is the biggest threat to the ecosystem of the Everglades. | | | |
| | Sample one-point response: Alligators make gator holes. Egrets eat fish. Humans threaten the Everglades. | | | |
| 2 | See rubric on p. T24. | U5L21: Research and Media Literacy: Interpret Information from Text Source | W.5.8 | 3 |
| | Sample two-point response: Source #3 would most likely be the most helpful source in understanding the process that leads to a place becoming a national park. It includes information about how the Everglades became a national park. Marjory Stoneman Douglas and others helped convince the United States government to create Everglades National Park. | | | |
| | Sample one-point response: Source #3 because it tells about how the Everglades became a national park. | | | |
| 3 | See answer below. | U5L25: Research and Media Literacy: Analyze Sources | RI.5.7 | 4 |
| | Dry Season: "Gater holes…", "Marshes become…", "Alligators move…", "Egrets build…"; Wet Season: "Egrets fly…", "Animals spread…" | | | |
| Essay Response | See rubric on p. T26. | U6L30: Writing: Informative | W.5.2 | 4 |

# Constructed-Response Rubrics

## READING Rubric

| | |
|---|---|
| **Score of 2** | • The response is logical and has an identifiable pattern/sequence.<br>• The response provides adequate evidence of the student's ability to interpret information and/or make inferences and conclusions about the passage.<br>• The response references clear evidence from the text that supports the student's response.<br>• The response includes specific examples and/or details that relate to the text. |
| **Score of 1** | • The response is logical and connected to the prompt but may lack an identifiable pattern/sequence.<br>• The response provides limited evidence of the student's ability to interpret information and/or make inferences and conclusions.<br>• The response references little evidence from the text that supports the student's response.<br>• The response includes some examples and/or details that relate to the text. |
| **Score of 0** | • The response provides no evidence of the student's ability to interpret information and/or make inferences and conclusions.<br>• The response includes no relevant information, evidence, or examples from the text. |

## WRITING Rubric

| | |
|---|---|
| **Score of 2** | • The response is logical, has an identifiable pattern/sequence, and is connected to the prompt.<br>• The response provides and incorporates sufficient key points, reasons, details, and/or evidence to support the student's response.<br>• The response includes elaboration and uses precise and specific words, language, and details. |
| **Score of 1** | • The response is mostly logical and connected to the prompt but may lack an identifiable pattern/sequence.<br>• The response provides and incorporates limited key points, reasons, details, and/or evidence to support the student's response.<br>• The response includes limited elaboration and uses general words, language, and details. |
| **Score of 0** | • The response has a weak or no connection to the prompt, may contradict the details/information in the prompt, or may restate provided details, introduce new or irrelevant details/information, or summarize the prompt.<br>• The response gives no or an inappropriate opinion/introduction/central idea/conclusion and provides few or no key points, reasons, details, and/or evidence.<br>• The response includes no elaboration and uses poor word choice. |

# Performance Task: Narrative Writing Rubric

| Score | 4 | 3 | 2 | 1 | NS |
|---|---|---|---|---|---|
| **Purpose/Organization** | The narrative is clear, focused, and well organized throughout. <br>• Contains an effective and complete plot <br>• Develops a strong setting, narrator/characters <br>• Includes a variety of transitions to connect ideas <br>• Contains a logical sequence of events <br>• Includes an effective introduction and conclusion | The narrative's organization is adequately maintained, and the focus is generally clear. <br>• Plot is mostly effective/may contain small flaws <br>• Develops setting/narrator/characters <br>• Adequate use of transitions to connect ideas <br>• Contains an adequate sequence of events <br>• Includes adequate introduction and conclusion | The narrative is somewhat organized and may be unclear in some parts. Plot may be inconsistent. <br>• Minimal development of setting, narrator/characters <br>• Inconsistent use of transitions to connect ideas <br>• Sequence of events is weak or unclear <br>• Introduction and conclusion need improvement | The narrative's focus and organization are not clear. <br>• Little or no plot <br>• Little or no development of setting, narrator/characters <br>• Contains few or inappropriate transitions and weak connections among ideas <br>• Sequence of events is not organized <br>• Introduction and/or conclusion may be missing | • Not intelligible <br>• Not written in English <br>• Not on topic <br>• contains text copied from source <br>• Does not address the purpose for writing |
| **Development/Elaboration** | The narrative includes effective elaboration using details, dialogue, and description. <br>• Characters, setting, experiences, and events are well developed <br>• Links to sources may enrich the narrative <br>• Writer uses a variety of narrative techniques that strengthen the story or illustrate the experience <br>• Contains effective sensory, concrete, and figurative language <br>• Style is appropriate and effective | The narrative includes adequate elaboration using details, dialogue, and description. <br>• Characters, setting, experiences, and events are adequately developed <br>• Links to sources may contribute to the narrative <br>• Writer uses a variety of narrative techniques that generally move the story forward and illustrate the experience <br>• Contains adequate sensory, concrete, and figurative language <br>• Style is mostly appropriate | The narrative includes partial or ineffective elaboration using unclear or inconsistent details, dialogue, and description. <br>• Characters, setting, experiences, and events lack consistent development <br>• Links to sources may be unsuccessful but do not detract from the narrative <br>• Writer uses inconsistent or weak narrative techniques <br>• Contains weak sensory, concrete, and figurative language <br>• Style is inconsistent or inappropriate | The narrative provides little or no elaboration using few or no details, dialogue, and description. <br>• Very little development of characters, setting, experiences, and events <br>• Links to sources, if present, may interfere with the narrative <br>• Writer's use of narrative techniques are minimal and may be incorrect <br>• Little or no sensory, concrete, and figurative language <br>• Little or no evidence of style | • Not intelligible <br>• Not written in English <br>• Not on topic <br>• contains text copied from source <br>• Does not address the purpose for writing |

| Score | 2 | 1 | 0 | NS |
|---|---|---|---|---|
| **Conventions** | The narrative demonstrates adequate command of conventions. <br>• Consistent use of correct sentence structures, punctuation, capitalization, grammar, and spelling | The narrative demonstrates partial command of conventions. <br>• Limited use of correct sentence structures, punctuation, capitalization, grammar, and spelling | The narrative demonstrates little or no command of conventions. <br>• Rare use of correct sentence structures, punctuation, capitalization, grammar, and spelling | • Not intelligible <br>• Not written in English <br>• Not on topic <br>• Contains text copied from source |

# Performance Task: Informative/Explanatory Writing Rubric

| Score | 4 | 3 | 2 | 1 | NS |
|---|---|---|---|---|---|
| **Purpose/Organization** | **The response is clear, focused, and well organized throughout.**<br>• Main or central idea is clear, focused, and effective for task, audience, and purpose<br>• Includes a variety of transitions to relate ideas<br>• Contains a logical sequence of ideas with strong relationships between them<br>• Includes an effective introduction and conclusion | **The response's organization is adequately maintained, and the focus is generally clear.**<br>• Main or central idea is clear, mostly focused, and mostly effective for task, audience, and purpose<br>• Includes some variety of transitions to relate ideas<br>• Contains an adequate sequence of ideas with adequate relationships between them<br>• Includes an adequate introduction and conclusion | **The response is somewhat focused but may be unclear in parts. Organization may be inconsistent.**<br>• Main or central idea may be somewhat unclear, may lack focus, or may be ineffective for task, audience, and purpose<br>• Includes little variety of transitions to relate ideas<br>• Sequence of ideas may be weak or unclear<br>• Introduction and conclusion need improvement | **The response's focus and organization are not clear.**<br>• Main or central idea may be confusing; response may be inappropriate for task, audience, and purpose<br>• Includes few or no transitions to relate ideas<br>• Sequence of ideas is unorganized; may include off-topic ideas<br>• Introduction and/or conclusion may be missing | • Not intelligible<br>• Not written in English<br>• Not on topic<br>• Contains text copied from source<br>• Does not address the purpose for writing |
| **Evidence/Elaboration** | **The response presents strong support for the main and supporting ideas with effective use of evidence from sources, facts, and details, elaborating with specific and effective language.**<br>• Evidence from sources is integrated, is relevant, and supports key ideas<br>• Writer uses a variety of elaborative techniques<br>• Vocabulary is clear and appropriate for task, audience, and purpose<br>• Style is appropriate and effective | **The response presents adequate support for the main and supporting ideas with evidence from sources, facts, and details, adequately elaborating with a mix of specific and general language.**<br>• Evidence from sources is integrated, is relevant, and adequately supports key ideas<br>• Writer uses some elaborative techniques<br>• Vocabulary is mostly appropriate for task, audience, and purpose<br>• Style is generally appropriate and effective | **The response presents inconsistent support for the main and supporting ideas with limited evidence from sources, facts, and details. Elaboration is inconsistent with simple language.**<br>• Evidence from sources may be poorly integrated or irrelevant, or only loosely supports key ideas<br>• Writer uses few elaborative techniques<br>• Vocabulary is somewhat inappropriate for task, audience, and purpose<br>• Style is largely ineffective | **The response presents little support for the main and supporting ideas with little or no evidence from sources, facts, or details. Elaboration is inadequate or absent.**<br>• Evidence from sources, if present, may be irrelevant with little support for key ideas<br>• Writer uses few or no elaborative techniques<br>• Vocabulary is inappropriate for task, audience, and purpose<br>• Style is weak or absent | • Not intelligible<br>• Not written in English<br>• Not on topic<br>• Contains text copied from source<br>• Does not address the purpose for writing |

| Score | 2 | 1 | 0 | NS |
|---|---|---|---|---|
| **Conventions** | **The response demonstrates adequate command of conventions.**<br>• Consistent use of correct sentence structures, punctuation, capitalization, grammar, and spelling | **The response demonstrates partial command of conventions.**<br>• Limited use of correct sentence structures, punctuation, capitalization, grammar, and spelling | **The response demonstrates little or no command of conventions.**<br>• Rare use of correct sentence structures, punctuation, capitalization, grammar, and spelling | • Not intelligible<br>• Not written in English<br>• Not on topic<br>• Contains text copied from source |

# Performance Task: Opinion Writing Rubric

## Purpose/Organization

| Score | Description |
|---|---|
| **4** | **The response is clear, focused, and well organized throughout.**<br>• Opinion is clear, focused, and effective for task, audience, and purpose<br>• Includes a variety of transitions to relate ideas<br>• Contains a logical sequence of ideas with strong relationships between them<br>• Includes an effective introduction and conclusion |
| **3** | **The response's organization is adequately maintained, and the focus is generally clear.**<br>• Opinion is clear, mostly focused, and mostly effective for task, audience, and purpose<br>• Includes some variety of transitions to relate ideas<br>• Contains an adequate sequence of ideas with adequate relationships between them<br>• Includes an adequate introduction and conclusion |
| **2** | **The response is somewhat focused, but may be unclear in parts. Organization may be inconsistent.**<br>• Opinion may be somewhat unclear, lack focus, or be ineffective for task, audience, and purpose<br>• Includes little variety of transitions to relate ideas<br>• Sequence of ideas may be weak or unclear<br>• Introduction and conclusion need improvement |
| **1** | **The response's focus and organization are not clear.**<br>• Opinion may be confusing; response may be inappropriate for task, audience, and purpose<br>• Includes few or no transitions to relate ideas<br>• Sequence of ideas is unorganized; may include off-topic ideas<br>• Introduction and/or conclusion may be missing |
| **NS** | • Not intelligible<br>• Not written in English<br>• Not on topic<br>• Contains text copied from source<br>• Does not address the purpose for writing |

## Evidence/Elaboration

| Score | Description |
|---|---|
| **4** | **The response presents strong support for the opinion with effective use of evidence from sources, facts, and details, elaborating with specific and effective language.**<br>• Evidence from sources is integrated, is relevant, and supports key ideas<br>• Writer uses a variety of elaborative techniques<br>• Vocabulary is clear and appropriate for task, audience, and purpose<br>• Style is appropriate and effective |
| **3** | **The response presents adequate support for the opinion with evidence from sources, facts, and details, adequately elaborating with a mix of specific and general language.**<br>• Evidence from sources is integrated, is relevant, and adequately supports key ideas<br>• Writer uses some elaborative techniques<br>• Vocabulary is mostly appropriate for task, audience, and purpose<br>• Style is generally appropriate and effective |
| **2** | **The response presents inconsistent support for the opinion with limited evidence from sources, facts, and details. Elaboration is inconsistent with simple language.**<br>• Evidence from sources may be poorly integrated or irrelevant or only loosely supports key ideas<br>• Writer uses few elaborative techniques<br>• Vocabulary is somewhat inappropriate for task, audience, and purpose<br>• Style is largely ineffective |
| **1** | **The response presents little support for the opinion with little or no evidence from sources, facts, or details. Elaboration is inadequate or absent.**<br>• Evidence from sources, if present, may be irrelevant, with little support for key ideas<br>• Writer uses few or no elaborative techniques<br>• Vocabulary is inappropriate for task, audience, and purpose<br>• Style is weak or absent |
| **NS** | • Not intelligible<br>• Not written in English<br>• Not on topic<br>• Contains text copied from source<br>• Does not address the purpose for writing |

## Conventions

| Score | Description |
|---|---|
| **2** | **The response demonstrates adequate command of conventions.**<br>• Consistent use of correct sentence structures, punctuation, capitalization, grammar, and spelling |
| **1** | **The response demonstrates partial command of conventions.**<br>• Limited use of correct sentence structures, punctuation, capitalization, grammar, and spelling |
| **0** | **The response demonstrates little or no command of conventions.**<br>• Rare use of correct sentence structures, punctuation, capitalization, grammar, and spelling |
| **NS** | • Not intelligible<br>• Not written in English<br>• Not on topic<br>• Contains text copied from source |

# Test Record Form

Student Name _____

## Assessment 1
Date _____

| Date Administered _____ | | Possible Score | Acceptable Score | Student Score |
|---|---|---|---|---|
| Reading (Items 1–20)* | Selected-Response | 18 | 16 | |
| | Constructed-Response | 4 | | |
| Writing (Items 21–30)* | Selected-Response | 9 | 8 | |
| | Constructed-Response | 2 | | |
| Listening (Items 31–39) | | 9 | 7 | |
| Research (Items 40–44) | | 5 | 4 | |
| | Total | 47 | 35 | |
| FINAL SCORE = Total Student Score x 2.12 = _____ | | | | |

## Performance Task 1
Date _____

| Date Administered _____ | | Possible Score | Acceptable Score | Student Score |
|---|---|---|---|---|
| Part 1 (Items 1–3)* | Selected-Response | 1 | 4 | |
| | Constructed-Response | 4 | | |
| Part 2 (Essay Response) | | 10 | 7 | |
| | Total | 15 | 11 | |
| Total Student Score x 6.67 = _____ | | | | |

## Assessment 2
Date _____

| Date Administered _____ | | Possible Score | Acceptable Score | Student Score |
|---|---|---|---|---|
| Reading (Items 1–20)* | Selected-Response | 18 | 16 | |
| | Constructed-Response | 4 | | |
| Writing (Items 21–30)* | Selected-Response | 9 | 8 | |
| | Constructed-Response | 2 | | |
| Listening (Items 31–39) | | 9 | 7 | |
| Research (Items 40–44) | | 5 | 4 | |
| | Total | 47 | 35 | |
| FINAL SCORE = Total Student Score x 2.12 = _____ | | | | |

## Performance Task 2
Date _____

| Date Administered _____ | | Possible Score | Acceptable Score | Student Score |
|---|---|---|---|---|
| Part 1 (Items 1–3)* | Selected-Response | 1 | 4 | |
| | Constructed-Response | 4 | | |
| Part 2 (Essay Response) | | 10 | 7 | |
| | Total | 15 | 11 | |
| Total Student Score x 6.67 = _____ | | | | |

## Assessment 3
Date _____

| Date Administered _____ | | Possible Score | Acceptable Score | Student Score |
|---|---|---|---|---|
| Reading (Items 1–20)* | Selected-Response | 18 | 16 | |
| | Constructed-Response | 4 | | |
| Writing (Items 21–30)* | Selected-Response | 9 | 8 | |
| | Constructed-Response | 2 | | |
| Listening (Items 31–39) | | 9 | 7 | |
| Research (Items 40–44) | | 5 | 4 | |
| | Total | 47 | 35 | |
| FINAL SCORE = Total Student Score x 2.12 = _____ | | | | |

## Performance Task 3
Date _____

| Date Administered _____ | | Possible Score | Acceptable Score | Student Score |
|---|---|---|---|---|
| Part 1 (Items 1–3)* | Selected-Response | 1 | 4 | |
| | Constructed-Response | 4 | | |
| Part 2 (Essay Response) | | 10 | 7 | |
| | Total | 15 | 11 | |
| Total Student Score x 6.67 = _____ | | | | |

*This section includes constructed-response items worth up to two points each. Please note when scoring.

**T28**

Name _____ Date _____

# Assessment 1
## Reading

**Read the text. Then answer the questions.**

# The Science Fair

Every year during the spring, our school holds a gigantic science fair. My best friend Rick was very proud of the project he was going to enter in the fair. He was certain that the worm house he was building would capture the blue ribbon.

The purpose of the worm house was to show how long it takes worms to eat different types of kitchen scraps. Rick's hypothesis, or the idea that he was trying to prove, was that worms eat and process some foods faster than others.

I am Rick's best friend, but I must admit that I was tired of hearing him bragging about his worm house. He talked about it *all* the time. I missed the old Rick who was always telling funny jokes and making me laugh. That friend constantly had me in stitches. "I can't wait until this science fair is over," I confessed to my mother.

"Maybe then Rick will finally start acting like himself again. He's become so serious that I can barely listen to him. All he ever talks about is that worm house!"

Finally, the day of the science fair arrived. As I set up my project, I kept one eye on Rick. As he started setting up the display board behind the worm house he seemed nervous, and that's when his problems started. Every time he let go of the board, it started to topple over. Rick was getting more and more distressed because he couldn't get the board to stay in place. Then, just when he thought he had finally succeeded, the board crashed down again, knocking the worm house onto the floor! Suddenly, dirt, wiggly worms, and scraps of old food flew everywhere. There were worms crawling all over the floor by Rick's feet. Rick's science fair project and hopes for victory were ruined.

At first, I couldn't help snickering a little as I viewed the mess, thinking Rick deserved this fate. But when I saw how upset he was, I stifled my laughter and offered to help him clean it up.

"I guess there's no chance of me winning the science fair now," Rick grumbled.

Name _____ Date _____

"Maybe you can change your project to something else," I suggested to my best friend.

Rick's face brightened as he looked at me. "Really? What can I change it to?" he asked.

"You can make a new hypothesis about how long it will take us to clean up this enormous mess!" I joked.

"That project might be even more interesting!"

Rick shot me a disappointed look that made me regret my silly joke. I felt bad for hurting his feelings.

Then a strange look slowly worked its way across his face. "Actually, that's a great idea," he said in that earnest tone that had me cringing for the last two weeks. "If each of us cleans up two handfuls every minute, how long do you think it will take us?"

My jaw dropped in disbelief. Rick wasn't actually going to try to figure this out, was he? I couldn't believe that he took my comments seriously! I looked up toward the ceiling wishing my old friend would miraculously return, when out of the corner of my eye, I saw Rick laughing at my horror-struck expression.

"Okay, you got me," I said with a shake of my head and a smile. My best friend, that old joking Rick, had never left!

Name _____ Date _____

**1** This question has two parts. First, answer part A. Then, answer part B.

**Part A**

Read the sentence from the text.

That friend constantly <u>had me in stitches</u>.

What does the phrase "had me in stitches" mean as it is used in the story?

Ⓐ  bothered me

Ⓑ  confused me

Ⓒ  made me laugh

Ⓓ  made me think

**Part B**

Which sentence from the passage **best** supports the answer to part A?

Ⓐ  "I am Rick's best friend, but I must admit that I was tired of hearing him bragging about his worm house."

Ⓑ  "He's become so serious that I can barely listen to him."

Ⓒ  "My best friend Rick was very proud of the project he was going to enter in the fair."

Ⓓ  "I missed the old Rick who was always telling funny jokes and making me laugh."

**2** From whose point of view is the passage told?

Ⓐ  Rick's

Ⓑ  Rick's friend's

Ⓒ  Rick's mother's

Ⓓ  Rick's friend's mother's

**3** Compare Rick's attitude at the beginning of the passage and at the end. How does he change?

Ⓐ  He becomes more serious.

Ⓑ  He returns to his old joking self.

Ⓒ  He decides to give up on science.

Ⓓ  He brags about his worm house.

**4** Underline the word in the passage that has a prefix that means "not."

My jaw dropped in disbelief. Rick wasn't actually going to try to figure this out, was he? I couldn't believe that he took my comments seriously! I looked up toward the ceiling wishing my old friend would miraculously return, when out of the corner of my eye, I saw Rick laughing at my horror-struck expression.

**5** How have Rick's and his best friend's feelings changed from the beginning of the story to the end of the story? Support your answer with details from the passage.

_____

_____

_____

_____

Name _____  Date _____

**Read the texts. Then answer the questions.**

# Valley Forge

In the fall of 1777, some American leaders criticized General George Washington for allowing the British to take Philadelphia, then the American capital. Washington did not let this criticism affect his decisions as a leader. Washington refused to be pushed into fighting battles he had no chance of winning. He looked for a place where his army could wait out the harsh winter and get needed training. He chose Valley Forge, Pennsylvania, not far from Philadelphia. Valley Forge had natural defenses and a water source. Army supplies were already stored there.

On December 12, 1777, Washington began to lead his army on a 13-mile march to Valley Forge. Snow, rain, sleet, and blocked roads turned the march into a nightmare. Many soldiers' uniforms were in tatters. Their shoes were falling apart. Some men even had no shoes at all.

On December 19, during a snowstorm, Washington's army arrived at Valley Forge. They were cold, tired, and hungry. Washington discovered that the British army had already seized the military supplies that had been stored there. They had even burned most of the houses. The American soldiers had to search for their own food. There was no shelter from the freezing cold.

Washington immediately ordered his commanding officers to divide their men into squads to build their own log huts. In the first couple of weeks, the soldiers built about two thousand huts. The huts provided shelter but were still drafty and damp.

The crowded, unhealthy conditions worried Washington. He ordered smallpox inoculations as a protection for the soldiers, to prevent this terrible disease from spreading.

The harsh weather had made the icy roads nearly impassable, and supplies did not arrive. The soldiers depended on "firecakes" made from flour and water. They hunted for deer, squirrels, rabbits, and other game animals.

Valley Forge was Washington's darkest hour and greatest challenge of the war. He knew that his soldiers might simply give up and go home. He had to persuade his officers and troops to serve the larger cause. Washington had to use his diplomatic skills to persuade Congress to collect needed funds from the states. He had to inspire trust and persuade others that victory was possible.

Name _____ Date _____

In February, a foreign visitor arrived at Valley Forge. Baron Friedrich von Steuben was an experienced officer in the German army. At Washington's request, von Steuben put the American troops on a training program.

Von Steuben saw that the soldiers were brave and not easily discouraged. Although many were excellent shots, they knew little about fighting together in battles. Von Steuben simplified the steps used for reloading muskets and ordered the soldiers to practice, practice, practice. Von Steuben was strict and demanding. He worked with the soldiers every day except Sunday, regardless of the weather. Some soldiers grumbled about the training, but most expressed admiration for the hard-working officer. Their sense of purpose grew stronger.

Congress helped Washington by appointing a capable quartermaster general in charge of supplies. General Nathanael Greene supervised road repair and organized farmers and suppliers in the area. Soon wagonloads of uniforms, boots, blankets, livestock, root vegetables, and new muskets were arriving in Valley Forge.

With the help of von Steuben and General Greene, Washington marched out of Valley Forge in June 1778 with an army that had been transformed. American troops were well trained, armed, and clothed. They were healthy and fit. They had more confidence than ever before.

# Father of the American Navy

Aboard the American warship the *Ranger* in the Irish Sea, Captain John Paul Jones sighted the British warship the *Drake*. Jones was determined to capture it.

It was April 1778, and the American colonies were fighting for independence from Britain. Though born in Scotland, Captain Jones was now an American soldier. The new United States had sent him across the ocean to make trouble for the British. It was a job that the daring captain was eager to take on, even though the British were a legendary naval power. The American navy, in contrast, had only a few small ships.

Drum rolls and pipes called the *Ranger*'s crew to their battle stations. Captain Jones directed all guns to fire at the *Drake*. When the *Drake* returned the shots, Jones stood on deck as officers were supposed to do, unmoving and unafraid. After the *Drake*'s captain and first officer were seriously wounded, the battle was soon over. "Quarter! Quarter!" the *Drake*'s sailing master called out—the cry of defeat.

It was "a truly gallant fight," Jones told his men. Under his leadership, inexperienced American sailors had captured a warship of the mighty British navy!

Eager for more victories, John Paul Jones took command of a better, faster ship, the *Bonhomme Richard*, the following year.

On September 23, 1779, the British warship the *Serapis*, commanded by Captain Pearson, was guiding merchant ships across the North Sea. The *Bonhomme Richard* began to chase after it. By five o'clock its prey was less than a mile away. On board drummers beat the signal for battle. Sailors rushed into position. The merchant ships escaped while the *Serapis* prepared to fight.

As the sun set, the two ships drew closer, and a furious battle erupted. Cannonballs knocked great holes in the sides of both ships. Two of the *Bonhomme Richard*'s cannons exploded. The *Serapis* had greater firepower, so Jones worked to bind his ship to the enemy's, side by side, to silence at least some of the cannons. Still, the *Serapis* fired all of its remaining firepower at the *Bonhomme Richard*.

With so many wounded and dying sailors on the American ship, it seemed as if the battle would soon be lost. Both ships were on fire, and the *Bonhomme Richard* was sinking. Through the thick smoke, American officer Henry Gardner could not see Captain Jones. Gardner thought that Jones must be dead. He cried out, "Quarter! Quarter!"

"Do you call for Quarter?" Captain Pearson shouted from the burning deck of the *Serapis*.

Suddenly, out of the smoke roared John Paul Jones. He is rumored to have defiantly replied, "I have not yet begun to fight!"

The battle continued. At last, a hand grenade from the *Bonhomme Richard* caused an explosion and multiple fires on the *Serapis*, and cannon fire cracked its main mast. Finally, after three and a half hours, Captain Pearson lowered his own flag and called for quarter. As the battered mast of his ship fell into the sea, Captain Pearson surrendered to the Americans.

The casualties were terrible on both sides. Probably half of each crew was dead or wounded. The *Bonhomme Richard*, beyond repair, was allowed to sink two days later. John Paul Jones took command of the *Serapis*. The Americans had achieved their most important naval victory.

For his role during the American Revolution, John Paul Jones became known as the "father of the American Navy."

**6** Read the sentence from "Valley Forge."

Congress helped Washington by appointing a capable quartermaster general in charge of supplies.

Which **two** events happened before this event?

Ⓐ The Army troops were well clothed.

Ⓑ Washington worried about his troops.

Ⓒ The American Army left Valley Forge.

Ⓓ Supplies could easily get into Valley Forge.

Ⓔ The Army troops were put on a training program.

**7** Read the sentence from "Valley Forge."

Washington discovered that the British army had already <u>seized</u> the military supplies that had been stored there.

What does the word <u>seized</u> mean as it is used in the sentence above?

Ⓐ used

Ⓑ stolen

Ⓒ released

Ⓓ organized

**8** Read the sentence from "Valley Forge."

He ordered smallpox <u>inoculations</u> as a protection for the soldiers, to prevent this terrible disease from spreading.

What does the word <u>inoculations</u> **most likely** mean?

Ⓐ a way to make soldiers able to survive cold conditions

Ⓑ something that protects people from illness

Ⓒ a shelter that prevents people from the rain

Ⓓ something that makes people sick

**9** Read the sentence from "Valley Forge."

> Valley Forge was Washington's <u>darkest hour</u> and greatest challenge of the war.

Which **two** sentences from the article does the author use to show the meaning of <u>darkest hour</u>?

Ⓐ "Washington discovered that the British had already seized the military supplies that had been stored there."

Ⓑ "They hunted for deer, squirrels, rabbits, and other game animals."

Ⓒ "Washington immediately ordered his commanding officers to divide their men into squads to build their own log huts."

Ⓓ "There was no shelter from the freezing cold."

Ⓔ "He knew that his soldiers might simply give up and go home."

**10** Which sentence from the article "Father of the American Navy" includes **two** words that begin with a Latin prefix that means "not"?

Ⓐ "Drum rolls and pipes called the *Ranger*'s crew to their battle stations."

Ⓑ "When the *Drake* returned the shots, Jones stood on deck as officers were supposed to do, unmoving and unafraid."

Ⓒ "After the *Drake*'s captain and first officer were seriously wounded, the battle was soon over."

Ⓓ "'Quarter! Quarter!' the *Drake*'s sailing master called out—the cry of defeat."

**11** Why does the author include Jones's defeat of the *Drake* in the article "Father of the American Navy"?

Ⓐ It showed that Britain had a powerful navy.

Ⓑ It proved that Jones could recruit sailors.

Ⓒ It showed that the British navy was not unbeatable.

Ⓓ It taught Jones to "stand tall" on deck during battle.

Name _____ Date _____

**12** Label the events from the "Father of the American Navy" in the order in which they happen. The first event will be labeled 1, and the last event will be labeled 5.

_____ The *Drake* surrenders.

_____ The *Serapis* escorts merchant ships.

_____ Captain Jones stops the lowering of the American flag.

_____ The *Bonhomme Richard* is burning.

_____ The sun sets on September 23, 1779.

**13** Which of the following statements is a central idea of "Father of the American Navy"?

Ⓐ Anyone can be a hero.

Ⓑ Hard work is more important than big dreams.

Ⓒ A good leader can help overcome a difficult situation.

Ⓓ Fighting in a war costs many lives.

**14** Compare the main problem and solution in "Valley Forge" and "Father of the American Navy." Is the problem described in the same way in each article? How do the authors use features like dialogue, formal text, and pacing to explain the problem each man faces? Include examples from the passages to support your answer.

_____

_____

_____

_____

**15** Which of the following can be found in **both** articles?

Ⓐ dialogue

Ⓑ idioms

Ⓒ humor

Ⓓ formal language

Name _____  Date _____

**Read the text. Then answer the questions.**

# The Picture Book

"Do you think you're a squirrel, or are you training to be an acrobat? Be careful; sometimes the trees aren't so nice!"

I giggled as Dad helped me down from the large sycamore tree in our yard.

"I just love the beautiful view, Dad!"

Dad continued, addressing no one in particular. "When Ella was born, I called her my little princess, and do you know what that makes me? The king!"

"Sorry, your majesty," I joked. "It appears you've raised a princess who loves to climb trees!" And then it happened, just as it had dozens of times before. Dad got a distant look in his eyes, and he raced off to work on his latest inspiration.

Dad writes children's books, and he says the idea for his next best-seller can pop into his head at any moment. Sometimes it's in the middle of the night. Sometimes it's in the middle of dinner. Sometimes it's in the middle of a conversation! I didn't see the possibilities for a story about squirrels, trees, acrobats, and princesses, but Dad says quirky ideas are what make a book appealing to children.

For a couple of weeks the sounds coming from Dad's office were a chorus of clicking keys and muttering, with an occasional "You're a genius!" Dad's not shy about giving himself a pat on the back. Finally, he announced he was finished writing.

The next day, with an elaborate bow, he asked, "Princess Ella, would you care to accompany me on a journey to Miss Lydia's studio?"

Miss Lydia is a children's book illustrator. She uses photographs of real people to help her with her drawings. During our visit she took lots of photographs of Dad and me for the illustrations in Dad's new book.

After that initial visit, we stopped by regularly to watch her progress. First, she did lots of rough sketches of our faces, of various poses, and of castles she found in books. All around the studio were piles of photographs and books about clothing, thrones, and crowns.

Next, Miss Lydia drew a storyboard, a series of little boxes on one piece of paper. She filled the boxes with tiny sketches showing what she planned to draw for each page.

Name _____ Date _____

After she finished the storyboard, she made a practice book, which she called a "dummy." In the dummy, Miss Lydia made pencil sketches that really looked like us!

At last, she started the final illustrations by painting in color—the ones that would be printed for the book. She used oil paints in beautiful deep, bright colors.

A few weeks later, Miss Lydia called. "I just finished the paintings," she said. "I want your approval before I send them off to the publisher."

The final paintings were fantastic! I couldn't believe the transformation. Not only did the king and the princess really look like us, but they looked like a historical king and princess, too. Miss Lydia had made the king's robe and the princess's dress look so beautiful, and she had painted on shoes and jewelry that looked real. Dad and I gasped when we saw the painting of the scared princess wandering around the angry trees. It was so lifelike—except the trees being angry, of course!

One Saturday morning a few months later, Miss Lydia joined Dad and me at our local bookstore to sign copies of *The Princess Who Loved to Climb Trees*. A large crowd gathered, and it seemed everyone commented on the same illustration. It was the one we had seen months ago in the studio, showing the scared princess (me!) walking among the angry trees. Unlike the princess, though, I wasn't scared. I was really excited!

---

**16** Which sentence from the passage has a word with a suffix that means "filled with"?

Ⓐ "I just love the beautiful view, Dad!"

Ⓑ "It appears you've raised a princess who loves to climb trees!"

Ⓒ "The final paintings were fantastic!"

Ⓓ "Unlike the princess, though, I wasn't scared."

Name _____  Date _____

**17** This question has two parts. First, answer part A. Then, answer part B.

**Part A**

From whose point of view is this story told?

(A) Ella's

(B) Dad's

(C) Miss Lydia's

(D) a narrator's not in the story

**Part B**

Read the paragraph from "The Picture Book." Underline the phrase in the paragraph that supports the answer to part A.

One Saturday morning a few months later, Miss Lydia joined Dad and me at our local bookstore to sign copies of *The Princess Who Loved to Climb Trees*. A large crowd had gathered, and it seemed everyone commented on the same illustration. It was the one we had seen months ago in the studio, showing the scared princess (me!) walking among the angry trees. Unlike the princess, though, I wasn't scared. I was really excited!

**18** Which statement **best** summarizes the central idea of "The Picture Book"?

(A) Writing a children's book is a difficult process.

(B) Illustrations are an important part of a book.

(C) Inspiration comes from many places.

(D) Family is the most important thing.

Name _____ Date _____

**19** Read the sentence from the passage.

After that <u>initial</u> visit, we stopped by regularly to watch her progress.

Which **two** words have the same meaning as the word <u>initial</u> as it is used in the sentence above?

Ⓐ final

Ⓑ first

Ⓒ important

Ⓓ introductory

Ⓔ last

Ⓕ necessary

**20** Read the paragraphs from the "The Picture Book." Underline the sentence that supports the theme "Great ideas can come from everyday events."

Dad continued, addressing no one in particular. "When Ella was born, I called her my little princess, and do you know what that makes me? The king!"

"Sorry, your majesty," I joked. "It appears you've raised a princess who loves to climb trees!" And then it happened, just as it had dozens of times before. Dad got a distant look in his eyes, and he raced off to work on his latest inspiration.

# Writing

**Read and answer each question.**

**21** Joe wrote a journal entry about his day on a farm. Read his journal entry. Underline the word that contains a spelling error.

> My brother and I had the best time at the farm that day. My grandfather was there to grete us in his loud voice. My grandmother says that Grandfather never has to repeat a word to anyone, anywhere. Grandfather took us in his rusty old truck to the pasture.

**22** Choose the sentence that contains a spelling error.

Ⓐ I sent her a quick replie.

Ⓑ The flowers smelled fresh and sweet.

Ⓒ The delivery man drove at top speed.

Ⓓ We saw steam coming from the engine.

**23** Jenna is writing a letter about singing in a show put on by her class. She wants to revise to eliminate any sentences that do not express a complete thought. Read the draft of a paragraph from her letter.

> I was petrified before I sang, but I knew I had to be brave. Other students in my class sang before I did, and they must have been dreadfully fearful, too. <u>When my turn came to walk onto the stage. I could hardly move.</u> My eyes pained me because the stage lights were dazzling and intense. Quaking and shuddering, I made my feet take me forward. When I did, the fear and anxiety ceased, and I sang as though it was easy. Afterward, everyone said that the show was an overwhelming success. I was elated to be a part of it.

Which revision is needed in the underlined sentences?

Ⓐ When my turn came to walk onto the stage; I could move.

Ⓑ When my turn came to walk onto the stage, I could hardly move.

Ⓒ When my turn came to walk the stage, and I could hardly move.

Ⓓ When my turn came to walk onto the stage, but I could hardly move.

Name _____ Date _____

**24** Which of the following sentences is punctuated correctly?

Ⓐ  The path follows the curve of the mountain?

Ⓑ  Is this the way to the soccer match?

Ⓒ  I think that is a great idea?

Ⓓ  Get us some ice cream?

**25** Which of the following sentences is correct?

Ⓐ  The Players walked to the field.

Ⓑ  We saw Valleys along the way.

Ⓒ  The Class decided to have a party.

Ⓓ  Mount Branson is the best place for hikers.

**26** Marilyn is writing a story about a dinner with her family. Read the draft of her second paragraph and complete the task that follows.

> Next, Margaret went to the kitchen. She liked the pleasurable odors of food cooking, especially when a turkey was roasting. Suddenly, Margaret heard almost earsplitting popping noises. She called Aunt Barbara, who rushed to the oven to discover a threatening situation. Margaret and Aunt Barbara saw dazzling orange flames <u>blowing higher</u> inside. Margaret started to shudder with anxiety. Then Aunt Barbara turned off the oven. The flames slowly disappeared, but there would be no turkey to eat that day.

Marilyn wants to replace the underlined words with a word that will make her meaning clearer. Which **three** words would be better choices?

Ⓐ  sliding

Ⓑ  spreading

Ⓒ  growing

Ⓓ  covering

Ⓔ  rising

Ⓕ  flickering

**27** A student is writing a story for class about the time he saw a shark. Read the draft. Underline **two** words that Jerry uses to show how he feels when he knows a shark is coming.

> I went into the water before I saw a huge gray thing coming toward me. Suddenly, when I finally saw it, I started to shake and shiver. It was a shark, swimming swiftly and urgently toward me. I did a double-take, turned, and swam faster than ever toward the shore.

**28** Alex is writing a note to his grandmother about a music class. Read his note.

> We had a lively music class today. A famous musician was in town, and our teacher invited him to play his guitar for us. The man sang in a gentle voice as he touched the strings with his long fingers. We all clapped loudly when he finished a song.

Which of the sentences in the note has the most sensory words?

(A) We had a lively music class today.

(B) A famous musician was in town, and our teacher invited him to play his guitar for us.

(C) The man sang in a gentle voice as he touched the strings with his long fingers.

(D) We all clapped loudly when he finished a song.

**29** You are writing about French chefs. You want to be very descriptive. Which of the following sentences is the best one to choose?

(A) French chefs create wonderful, good, delicious food.

(B) French chefs who create tasty dishes look good and taste delicious.

(C) French chefs create interesting dishes that look good and taste delicious.

(D) French chefs create interesting dishes when they look good and taste delicious.

**Assessment 1**
17
**Grade 5**

Name _____ Date _____

**30** Leroy wrote about the time he visited a museum. Read the first paragraph of his story. Rewrite the paragraph to be more descriptive. Be sure to include vivid details and sensory words.

> Every summer, I go on a vacation with my grandparents. We always visit at least one museum or research site, and this year, we chose to visit a museum of art. My friend Joey said, "That sounds almost painfully dull." I know you, too, would say it was uneventful. But I really enjoyed seeing all of the paintings.

_____

_____

_____

_____

Name _____ Date _____

# Listening

**Listen to the presentation. Then answer the questions.**

# Tempest over Tea Parties

THE DESTRUCTION OF TEA AT BOSTON HARBOR.

Name _____ Date _____

**31** The British thought that the colonists would not object to paying the tea tax of 1773. Which detail **best** supports this conclusion?

Ⓐ People stopped British ships from unloading.

Ⓑ The colonists could use the tea tax as a symbol.

Ⓒ The Tea Act of 1773 would benefit a British company.

Ⓓ It was not a new tea tax and it would be temporary.

**32** Which **two** conclusions are supported by "Tempest over Tea Parties"?

Ⓐ People in other seaport cities supported Boston colonists who resisted the Tea Act of 1773.

Ⓑ The Boston colonists thought the ships should anchor in another seaport city.

Ⓒ The colonists used the Tea Act of 1773 as a symbol of resistance to the British.

Ⓓ Mohawk people boarded the ship with one hundred Boston colonists.

Ⓔ George Hewes heard about the Boston Tea Party years after it happened.

**33** The following question has two parts. First, answer part A. Then, answer part B.

**Part A**

Which conclusion is supported by "Tempest over Tea Parties"?

Ⓐ Tea ships often sailed from London in December.

Ⓑ The Boston Tea Party was the first incident to occur in a seaport city.

Ⓒ The British refused the colonists' demands to sail to other seaport cities.

Ⓓ The colonists who boarded the ship were afraid that the British would find out their names.

**Part B**

Which detail from "Tempest over Tea Parties" supports your answer in part A?

Ⓐ The colonists resisted being taxed by the British government.

Ⓑ George Hewes recalled how the men boarded the British ships.

Ⓒ The colonists' action against the Tea Act of 1773 became known as the Boston Tea Party.

Ⓓ The colonists boarded the ships at night and disguised themselves as Mohawk people.

Listen to the presentation. Then answer the questions.

# The Tea Boycotts

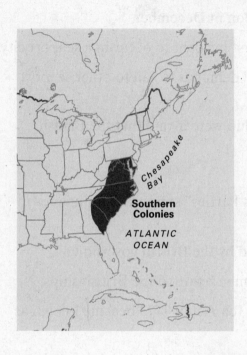

**34** In 1774, American women discovered that they had an important role to play in patriotic protests. Which detail from "The Tea Boycotts" **best** supports this conclusion?

Ⓐ The women of Edenton, North Carolina, signed a political declaration against drinking tea.

Ⓑ Women joined the colonial assembly of Edenton, North Carolina.

Ⓒ Colonists organized boycotts in many places.

Ⓓ Women served "liberty tea."

**35** In 1774, the colonial assembly of Edenton, North Carolina, supported a boycott of British tea. Which detail from "The Tea Boycotts" **best** supports this conclusion?

Ⓐ Colonists refused to pay the cost of the British tea.

Ⓑ Groups of women organized boycotts in many places.

Ⓒ Edenton women signed a political declaration not to conform to the custom of drinking tea.

Ⓓ Edenton women signed a political declaration that supported the colonial assembly's boycott of British tea.

Name _____ Date _____

**36** The following question has two parts. First, answer part A. Then, answer part B.

## Part A

Which conclusion is supported by "The Tea Boycotts"?

Ⓐ The Edenton women organized boycotts at Boston.

Ⓑ In 1774, colonial women had more political freedom than British.

Ⓒ "Liberty tea" was a mixture of smuggled tea and local plants.

Ⓓ The Edenton colonists borrowed a recipe from the American Indians.

## Part B

Which detail from the presentation supports your answer in part A?

Ⓐ In 1774, the colonists refused to pay the cost of the tea.

Ⓑ Creative cooks boiled up local plants to make tea substitutes.

Ⓒ Edenton, North Carolina, was the place for women to organize boycotts.

Ⓓ Many Americans admired the Edenton women whose declaration shocked the British.

Name _____ Date _____

**Listen to the presentation. Then answer the questions.**

# James Otis

**37** Which **two** conclusions are supported by the passage "James Otis"?

Ⓐ Otis defended a law that allowed the British to search colonists' homes.

Ⓑ Otis argued that taxation without representation is tyranny.

Ⓒ Adams helped to plant the seeds of the American Revolution.

Ⓓ The British enforced the law to allow searches of colonists' homes.

Ⓔ Adams named the case of 1761 as the first act of resistance to British policies.

Ⓕ Otis won many cases for the American colonists in the later years of his career.

**38** James Otis played a major role in the resistance that led to the American Revolution. Which detail from "James Otis" **best** supports this conclusion?

Ⓐ Otis spoke out against many British policies.

Ⓑ In 1761, Otis delivered a five-hour speech against tyranny.

Ⓒ Otis argued that customs officers did not have the right to search homes.

Ⓓ Adams, future President of the United States, was at the court in 1761.

**39** Read the sentence from the passage.

Although Otis lost the case, the British did not want to make the public angry by enforcing the law.

Which conclusion can be drawn from this sentence?

Ⓐ It didn't matter to Otis if he won or lost.

Ⓑ The British thought Otis should have won.

Ⓒ The British used the case to judge public opinion.

Ⓓ The British thought Americans were unpredictable.

Name _____ Date _____

# Research

**Read and answer each question.**

**40** A student is writing a research report about gravity on Mars. The student needs to find more information for his report. Which source would **most likely** have more information about gravity on Mars?

Ⓐ www.voyagetomars.org

A website about the plan to send humans to Mars in the twenty-first century

Ⓑ *Earth and Mars: The Difference in Gravity*

A book that compares gravity on many planets

Ⓒ *How Gravity Works*

A book for kids about the basic principles of gravity

Ⓓ "Finding Mars in the Night Sky"

An article in a local newspaper about using a telescope to locate Mars

Name _____ Date _____

**41** A student is writing a report about different kinds of puppet theater. The student found several sources. Which sources would **most likely** have information for the report? Choose **two** sources.

Ⓐ  *Theater History*

A textbook covering theater history from the Ancient Greeks to the present day

Ⓑ  www.punchandjudy.com

A website about the history of the puppets Punch and Judy and how they were used in theater

Ⓒ  www.becominganactor.net

A website that offers tips for young actors who want to make a career for themselves in theater

Ⓓ  "Make a Puppet in Six Easy Steps"

A magazine article about how to make a puppet easily from simple materials

Ⓔ  www.fingerpuppetsfortoddlers.com

A website that shows how to use finger puppets to amuse young children

Ⓕ  *Puppet Theaters of the World*

A book that describes puppet theaters in India, Indonesia, the United States, and other countries

**42** A student has made a plan for research. It includes this research question: What is the best strategy for winning a school election? Which sources would **most likely** be the best sources for the information needed to answer the research question? Choose **two** sources.

ⓐ www.campaignposters.com

A website with step-by-step instructions for making campaign posters

ⓑ *School Elections: Then and Now*

A book about the history of school elections in America

ⓒ "How We Won"

A magazine article about how three different class presidents won their school elections

ⓓ www.studentgovernment.edu

An online forum that brings different student governments together to share ideas

ⓔ www.tipsforwinning.com

A website with suggestions from experts about how to win school elections

ⓕ *My Life in Politics*

A biography about a senator whose interest in politics began in middle school when he ran for class president

Name _____ Date _____

**43** A student is writing a report about how pea plants grow. She found a diagram. Look at the diagram and read the directions that follow.

The student found a second source. Read the second source. Underline **two** sentences from the second source that support the information in the diagram.

The life cycle of a pea plant begins when you first place the pea seed in the ground. It is especially important that the dirt be moist at this stage, which allows the plant to grow. First, a root will begin to grow from the seed. This root will dig deep into the soil to help keep the plant steady. Later, shoots and leaves will grow upward, but it will take some time. Eventually the pea plants can grow to be 5 feet tall or more!

**44** A student is writing a report about story structure. He found a table. Look at the table and read the directions that follow.

### Story Structure

| Name | Length | Position |
|------|--------|----------|
| Rising Action | Long | Beginning: ends at climax |
| Climax | Instant | Closer to the end |
| Falling Action | Short | From climax to end |

The student found a second source. Read the second source. Underline **two** sentences from the second source that support the information in the diagram.

Writing a short story can be a lot of fun! Before you start, it helps to know something about story structure. Most stories begin by introducing the main character and a problem that the character has. Then the character tries to solve his or her problem. The action reaches a climax when the problem is solved or not. This is usually the most exciting part of the story! The parts of the story before and after the climax are called rising and falling action.

# Performance Task 1

## Part 1

# Exploring Space

**Task:**

Your science class takes a trip to the planetarium. An instructor describes the history of space travel in the United States. The instructor also shares some of the possibilities for the future of space travel. You and your classmates become interested in learning more about space travel. During your research, you find three more articles about this topic.

After you have looked at these sources, you will answer some questions about them. Briefly scan the sources and the three questions that follow. Then go back and read the sources carefully so you will have the information you need to answer the questions and complete your research. You may use scratch paper to take notes on information you find in the sources you read.

In Part 2, you will write a story using the information you read.

**Directions for Beginning:**

You will now look at several sources. You can look at any of the sources as often as you like.

**Research Questions:**

After reviewing the sources, use the rest of the time in Part 1 to answer three questions about them. Your answers to these questions will be scored. Also, your answers will help you think about the information you read, which should help you write your narrative story.

You may refer back to your scratch paper to review your notes when you think it would be helpful. Answer the questions in the spaces below the items.

Your written notes on scratch paper will be available to you in Part 1 and Part 2 of the performance task.

Name _____ Date _____

**Source #1**

You found an article that tells about President Kennedy's goal of sending a human to the moon.

# Apollo to the Moon

On May 25, 1961, President John F. Kennedy spoke to Congress. He said, "I believe this nation should commit itself to achieving the goal, before this decade is out, of landing a man on the moon and returning him safely to Earth."

The National Aeronautics and Space Administration was put in charge. NASA launched the effort. It was called Project Apollo. Two other projects were started to gather more information. This information was important to have before the Apollo project could begin.

NASA set up Project Mercury to choose and train astronauts. NASA tested more than one hundred pilots. Only eighteen pilots passed all the tests. Seven were chosen to become the Mercury astronauts. The astronaut trainees went to survival training in the desert. They suffered heat and cold. They were placed into a training machine and flipped upside down over and over again.

Project Mercury then began testing the ability of humans to survive in space and return safely to Earth. On May 5, 1961, Alan Shepard became the first American in space. On February 20, 1962, John Glenn became the first American to orbit Earth. In all, there were six flights with crews. The number of orbits increased. Flights grew longer. On May 15, 1963, Gordon Cooper spent more than a day in space. All of these flights helped NASA prepare for future space travel.

Project Gemini tested new equipment. It also provided training in a series of flights to help NASA find answers to questions. Could astronauts work outside a spacecraft? Could two spacecraft meet in space? Could they dock with each other? How would a long stay in space affect astronauts? The Project Gemini space flights and tests between 1964 and 1966 helped answer these questions. NASA moved forward with Project Apollo and the goal of landing a human on the moon before the end of the 1960s.

Finally, as part of the Apollo project, on July 16, 1969, *Apollo 11* lifted off for the moon. Millions of people around the world followed its trip. The members of its crew were Neil Armstrong, Mike Collins, and Buzz Aldrin. They would soon be making history! On July 20, everyone at NASA's Mission Control in Houston, Texas, waited to hear from the crew. They were thrilled to hear Armstrong's simple message, "The Eagle has landed." Six hours later, Armstrong climbed down Eagle's ladder. He stepped onto the moon, and spoke words that would live forever. "That's one small step for a man," he said, "one giant leap for mankind." This first team of astronauts contributed to people's knowledge of space. The mission had fulfilled President Kennedy's dream to put humans on the moon!

---

**Source #2**
You found an article about the first female African American astronaut.

# Mae Jemison, Astronaut

As a young child, Mae Jemison clearly remembers listening to Mission Control's final countdowns: 5, 4, 3, 2, 1, and liftoff! She remembers thinking that someday she would be on a shuttle headed to space. That someday came on September 12, 1992. Television screens around the world showed the liftoff of the space shuttle *Endeavour*. Jemison was on board. She was the first African American woman to fly in space.

Since 1981 NASA had been sending crews of astronauts into space on space shuttles. Space shuttles were large, winged aircraft that launched as rockets into space. After each mission, the shuttle could return to Earth. It would land just like an airplane.

Mae Jemison was born in Alabama in 1956. Her family moved to Chicago when she was three years old. As a child, she was always interested in science. She spent many hours in the library reading about different scientific topics. Stars and constellations were among her favorite subjects. Mae entered many citywide science fairs. She won first prize for most of them.

Mae was only twelve years old when she started high school. She was just sixteen when she went to college. She attended Stanford University in California and then went to medical school in New York. After graduation she worked for the Peace Corps in West Africa. She then became a doctor in Los Angeles. Although she loved helping people, she hadn't forgotten her dream of becoming an astronaut.

Dr. Jemison applied to NASA to become an astronaut. After the space shuttle *Challenger* exploded in 1986, the U.S. space program was put on hold. NASA did not need any new astronauts for a while. Jemison knew about the dangers that astronauts faced, but she wasn't afraid. She reapplied for the program in 1987 and was accepted.

In 1992, Jemison was a science mission specialist aboard the space shuttle *Endeavour.* It carried a laboratory called Spacelab-J. The eight-day trip was a joint mission by Japan and the United States. Jemison and six other scientists tested the effects of weightlessness in space. They tested this on humans and on creatures, such as flies, hornets, fish, and frogs.

Dr. Jemison left NASA after six years. One of her projects since then has been to run an international science camp for students. The goal of the camp was to improve students' understanding of science and increase their problem-solving skills. The camp was named The Earth We Share. At the camp, campers work together to identify possible solutions to global problems.

Mae Jemison has led a truly remarkable life. Her incredible accomplishments have added to what we now know about space. Her desire to share what she has learned has been helpful to generations. She has inspired many young people to do as she did and reach for the stars!

**Source #3**
You found an article about the different types of spacecraft used for missions.

# Spacecraft: From Module to Shuttle

Space exploration has significantly changed since it began. Some of the biggest changes were the vehicles that astronauts used to travel into space. Early programs used modules launched on rockets, but eventually NASA developed space shuttles.

The first project that took Americans into space was Project Mercury, which lasted from 1961 to 1963. It used a spacecraft called the *Mercury Capsule*. The capsule was very small, able to fit only one person who had to remain seated. The *Mercury Capsule* was launched using a rocket built by the military.

In 1965 Project Gemini began. It also used a capsule; however, it was slightly larger. It could hold two astronauts.

The Apollo program had its initial flight in 1968. Astronauts traveled to the moon on the Apollo missions. They traveled in the *Apollo Command Module*, which held three passengers. Another spacecraft, the *Lunar Module*, was used in the Apollo mission. It was used to actually land on the moon. The Apollo mission lasted until 1972. During this time, twelve astronauts walked on the moon and studied its surface.

Until 1981, all spacecraft could be used only once. Then the space shuttle was designed. It had three main parts: the orbiter, the external tank, and the rocket boosters. The space shuttle launched like the rockets of the past, but it landed just like an airplane! The space shuttle was the first vehicle designed to travel to space up to one hundred times. This was a huge advancement in technology and was designed to save money. This money could then be used for more missions, as well as more research. It was also much larger and could carry up to seven astronauts at a time. From 1981 to 2011 there were 135 missions launched on five space shuttles. The names of the space shuttles were *Columbia, Challenger, Discovery, Atlantis,* and *Endeavour.* In 2011 NASA's space shuttle program completed its final mission. NASA ended the program and retired the shuttle fleet.

Name _____ Date _____

    Space travel for the future is being planned right now. NASA is researching how to send astronauts to the planet Mars. What will their spacecraft look like? We can only wait and see!

_____

**1** Source #1 and Source #2 discuss how two people helped make advances in the exploration of space. Explain how these two individuals made a difference in the field of space exploration. Use at least **one** detail from Source #1 and **one** detail from Source #2 to support your answer. For each detail, include the source title or number.

_____

_____

_____

_____

_____

Name _____ Date _____

**2** Which source would **most likely** be the most helpful in understanding the different methods of space travel used throughout the years? Explain why this source is **most likely** the most helpful. Give at least **two** details from the source to support your answer.

_____

_____

_____

_____

**3** Mark the boxes to match each source with the idea or ideas that it supports. Some ideas may have more than one source selected.

|  | Source #1: Apollo to the Moon! | Source #2: Mae Jemison, Astronaut | Source #3: Spacecraft: From Module to Shuttle |
|---|---|---|---|
| Women have played an important role in space exploration. |  |  |  |
| Astronauts make trips that improve people's understanding of space science. |  |  |  |
| Project Apollo was a successful project that increased people's knowledge about the moon and its surface. |  |  |  |

Name _____ Date _____

# Part 2

You will now review your notes and sources, and plan, draft, revise, and edit your writing. You may use your notes and go back to your sources. Now read your assignment and the information about how your writing will be scored, then begin your work.

**Your Assignment:**

Your teacher wants you to use the research information you gathered about the history of space travel for a class project. For your part in the project, you are assigned to write a story that is several paragraphs long about what would happen if you were an astronaut who traveled on one of the space missions that you have researched.

In your story, you will be an astronaut. You will prepare for and then participate in a mission into space. Describe how you prepare, how you get into space, and what you do once you are there. When writing your story, find ways to use information and details from the sources to improve your story. Make sure you develop your characters, setting, and the plot. Also use details, dialogue, and description where appropriate.

**REMEMBER: A well-written narrative story**
- has an effective and complete plot.
- is well-organized and clear.
- has an introduction and conclusion.
- has a logical sequence of events.
- uses transitions.
- develops a setting, narrator/characters, and point of view.
- uses description, details, and dialogue.
- has effective and appropriate style.
- uses details from the sources to support your story.
- follows rules of writing (spelling, punctuation, grammar usage).

Now begin your work on your story. Manage your time carefully so that you can

- plan your multi-paragraph story.
- write your multi-paragraph story.
- revise and edit the final draft of your multi-paragraph story.

Name _____ Date _____

For Part 2, you are being asked to write a narrative story that is several paragraphs long. Write your response in the space below.

Remember to check your notes and your prewriting and planning as you write, and then revise and edit your story.

_____

_____

_____

_____

_____

_____

_____

_____

_____

_____

_____

_____

_____

_____

_____

_____

_____

_____

_____

_____

_____

_____

_____

_____

42

Name _____ Date _____

Name _____ Date _____

_____

_____

_____

_____

_____

_____

_____

_____

_____

_____

_____

_____

_____

_____

_____

_____

_____

_____

_____

_____

_____

_____

_____

Name _____    Date _____

# Assessment 2
## Reading

Read the text. Then answer the questions.

# Kayaking Alaska

"Kayaking in Alaska, best vacation ever!" said Melinda as she grinned at Julio over the top of the brochure she was reading. Melinda was excited about the family vacation, but Julio was not. She showed him a picture of a glacier and a seal, but he ignored her.

"Why can't we go to SciFi Land in California?" asked Julio as he slid his fingers across the game controls on his digital tablet. The theme park had been his preferred vacation spot. On one of the rides, an army of hologram droids chase you! But Mom and Dad had made their decision, and they wanted Julio and Melinda to experience the beauty of nature. "Can we at least go to SciFi Land next year?" Julio asked, but he was disappointed by his mother's reply.

"We'll cross that bridge when we come to it," she replied.

Two days later, the family disembarked from their plane in Anchorage. They were whisked away to their hotel in a taxi. The next morning, they were met by a driver who took them to a village on Prince William Sound. There they were dropped off with their kayaks and supplies. The guide waiting for them was young with a kind face; he helped them put on life jackets and pack their kayaks.

"Now we're going to have a good time, but we need to remember to be cautious," said the guide, focusing his attention on Melinda and Julio. He warned them to be careful near glaciers. Gigantic chunks of ice often fell off and landed in the water. "You don't want to be too near the waves created by those monsters!" The guide smiled, but Julio could tell the guide was serious.

"Great!" said Julio with a glum look on his face. "We'll be seeing Alaska from the bottom of the ocean!" He looked at the gear piled in the kayaks and the frigid water in front of them.

The guide laughed. "I don't think that will be a problem as long as you stay close to me. Get ready because there's a lot of wildlife to see."

Julio and Mom slipped into one kayak, and Melinda and Dad paddled off in the other. The guide had his own kayak and led the family out into the water. "This is going to be fun!" said Melinda as she and Dad shot off ahead.

Julio sighed and paddled slowly after them. That first day, the family saw a mother bear and her two cubs fishing at the edge of the water. When Julio's kayak floated just a little too close, the mother bear reared up on her hind legs and roared, scaring the daylights out of Julio, who paddled so fast to get away that he felt his arms would fall off. On the afternoon of the second day, the family was nearly doused by the spray of a humpback whale that breached not 20 yards from where they paddled! Melinda got a good photograph as the whale flipped its tail high out of the water and disappeared beneath the surface; she also took a photograph of Julio's surprised face.

"That's more thrilling than any theme park ride, don't you think?" Melinda called out to Julio hopefully.

"Yeah, awesome!" he said, shooting her a sarcastic, nervous smile. He glanced around cautiously to see what else might emerge suddenly from the water, though for the moment, nothing did.

On the final day of the trip, the family came to a glacier, and as they paddled nearby, big chunks of ice broke off the ice face, sounding like thunder. The kayakers were far enough away not to be flipped over by the waves, but the undulating water made the kayaks bob up and down wildly.

"Whoa!" cried Julio with a giant smile, as he and Mom rode the waves. "It's like a roller coaster!"

"Told you!" called Melinda from her kayak, steadying her camera to take his picture, and, for once, he smiled.

"You're right!" Julio replied as he looked at the beauty around him. "Nature is the best theme park in the world!"

Name _____ Date _____

**1** This question has two parts. First, answer part A. Then, answer part B.

**Part A**

According to the text, what event causes a change in the way Julio feels about the kayaking trip?

Ⓐ getting sprayed by a whale

Ⓑ paddling until his arms are tired

Ⓒ riding the waves like a roller coaster

Ⓓ seeing a mother bear on her hind legs

**Part B**

Choose the detail from the text which best shows the change caused by the event in part A.

Ⓐ "Why can't we go to SciFi Land in California?" asked Julio.

Ⓑ "Great!" said Julio with a glum look on his face. "We'll be seeing Alaska from the bottom of the ocean!"

Ⓒ "Yeah, awesome!" he said, shooting her a sarcastic, nervous smile.

Ⓓ "You're right!" Julio replied as he looked at the beauty around him. "Nature is the best theme park in the world!"

**2** Read the sentence from the text.

"We'll cross that bridge when we come to it," she replied.

What does the phrase <u>we'll cross that bridge when we come to it</u> **most likely** mean?

Ⓐ It's a good idea to plan for the future.

Ⓑ If we get to a crossing, we can walk over it.

Ⓒ We will delay the decision until it is necessary.

Ⓓ We need to try harder to enjoy our time together.

Name _____ Date _____

**3** Read the sentence from the text.

"Now we're going to have a good time, but we need to remember to be cautious," said the guide.

The word cautious is **most similar** in meaning to what other word?

Ⓐ lazy

Ⓑ wild

Ⓒ thankful

Ⓓ watchful

**4** According to the text, what word **best** describes Melinda's character?

Ⓐ kind

Ⓑ nervous

Ⓒ impatient

Ⓓ adventurous

**5** Read the following paragraph from the text. Underline an example of a simile.

On the final day of the trip, the family came to a glacier, and as they paddled nearby, big chunks of ice broke off the ice face, sounding like thunder. The kayakers were far enough away not to be flipped over by the waves, but the undulating water made the kayaks bob up and down wildly.

**Read the text. Then answer the questions.**

# Bear Country

Early in the evening, a homeowner in an American town fills the backyard bird feeder with sunflower seeds. Not long afterward, a black bear emerges from a wooded area and walks across the lawn. Family members watch in amazement from their living room window. They had no idea that bears lived in their neighborhood! The bear knocks down the bird feeder with one swipe. The bear sits and gobbles the seeds. Then it shuffles off, back into the trees.

This family has had an experience that is less unusual than you might think. Human-bear encounters are increasingly taking place in the suburbs and towns of North America.

The American black bear is the most common bear in North America. Its territory includes almost all of Canada, most of the United States, and parts of northern Mexico.

Black bears are often black but may also be cinnamon brown, and some are even white. Though smaller than grizzly bears, black bears can grow to weigh six hundred pounds. They have a shuffling gait but can move quickly when necessary. Black bears are strong swimmers. They are expert climbers, capable of climbing a tree in a few quick leaps.

Black bears are animals of the forest. But their woodland habitats have been reduced because of human encroachment. People have cut down trees to develop land for homes, industry, and roads. As a result, bears have adapted to living close to people, and the number of bear sightings in populated areas is growing.

Black bears, like most bears, are omnivores. They will eat almost anything: primarily nuts, fruits, berries, and insect larvae. They sometimes eat dead animals and the young of deer and moose. Black bears also eat food left out by humans. Their keen sense of smell leads them to campsites, pet food, and garbage cans.

Because bears are quite intelligent and have long memories, they will return again and again to places where they have found food. In times when bears can't find enough food in the woods, they look for it closer to humans.

Black bears are naturally shy, but if a bear loses its fear of people, it can become a real nuisance. People are understandably afraid of a large, powerful wild animal near their homes.

A bear is strong enough to break down a door and cause other property damage. Black bear attacks on humans are extremely rare, but a nervous, frightened bear that has no escape route could nip or slap, causing injury.

Human-bear encounters are most likely to occur in spring, when bears emerge from their winter dens and head out to find food and mates. Wildlife specialists promote taking steps to avoid conflicts with bears. The most important rule to follow is this: Do not feed the bears!

To avoid feeding bears unintentionally, store all garbage in containers with tight-fitting lids. Put the containers out on the morning of trash-collection day. Wash garbage containers with disinfectant to remove odors. Don't leave bird feeders out at night, and clean up any spilled seeds. Avoid leaving pet food or pet bowls outdoors, and clean and store outdoor grills.

What should you do if you encounter a black bear? Don't panic and run because a bear may instinctively give chase. Instead, back up slowly, speaking in a low, calm voice. Avoid looking directly at the bear's eyes, and make sure it has an escape route.

**6** Which of the following **best** explains the main purpose of this text?

Ⓐ to explain why bears are dangerous

Ⓑ to inform readers about bear behaviors

Ⓒ to teach readers about what to feed bears

Ⓓ to persuade readers to stay away from bears

**7** Select the **three** statements that **best** describe the black bear behaviors that can affect humans living close to them.

Ⓐ Black bears are strong swimmers.

Ⓑ Black bears will eat food left outside.

Ⓒ Black bears can grow to weigh six hundred pounds.

Ⓓ Black bears have adapted to living near settlements.

Ⓔ Black bears are intelligent and return to the places they find food.

**8** The author suggests that humans may be responsible for a growing number of bear sightings. Explain why humans may be responsible, and include a piece of evidence to support your explanation.

_____

_____

_____

_____

_____

**9** Read the sentence from the text.

Wildlife specialists promote taking steps to avoid conflicts with bears.

In the word promote, what does the prefix "*pro-*" mean?

Ⓐ a job

Ⓑ to favor

Ⓒ to prove

Ⓓ a positive

Name _____ Date _____

**10** Read the paragraphs from the text. Underline one sentence that shows a cause-and-effect statement.

Black bears, like most bears, are omnivores. They will eat almost anything: primarily nuts, fruits, berries, and insect larvae. They sometimes eat dead animals and the young of deer and moose. Black bears also eat food left out by humans. Their keen sense of smell leads them to campsites, pet food, and garbage cans.

Because bears are quite intelligent and have long memories, they will return again and again to places where they have found food. In times when bears can't find enough food in the woods, they look for it closer to humans.

Black bears are naturally shy, but if a bear loses its fear of people, it can become a real nuisance. People are understandably afraid of a large, powerful wild animal near their homes.

**11** Reread the conclusion paragraph. In one sentence, summarize the advice the author offers to the reader.

What should you do if you encounter a black bear? Don't panic and run because a bear may instinctively give chase. Instead, back up slowly, speaking in a low, calm voice. Avoid looking directly at the bear's eyes, and make sure it has an escape route.

_____
_____
_____
_____
_____

**Read the text. Then answer the questions.**

# Meriwether Lewis

Meriwether Lewis was a member of one of the most famous partnerships in American history. He and William Clark led the Corps of Discovery, a team of explorers who traveled through the American Northwest.

Their journey began in 1804 and lasted 28 months. It fulfilled the goals set out by President Thomas Jefferson. The Corps found a route to the Pacific Ocean and made detailed maps. The explorers reported on landforms, waterways, weather, plants, and animals, as well as people and cultures. The journey is known as the Lewis and Clark Expedition.

Meriwether Lewis was born in 1774 and spent his early years on his family's Virginia plantation. One of his neighbors was Thomas Jefferson, a leading figure in the colonists' fight for independence from Britain. Meriwether's father served as a soldier in the Revolutionary War and died from illness before the war ended. At the time, Meriwether was five years old.

Meriwether's mother remarried, and the family moved to the Georgia frontier when Meriwether was about nine years old. In this unsettled region, Meriwether hiked and hunted and learned about the natural world. His mother knew the medicinal uses of many wild plants and shared her knowledge with her son, who was an eager student.

Seeking a formal education, Meriwether returned to Virginia at age thirteen to attend school and to learn to run the family's plantation. After his stepfather died, in 1791, Meriwether quit school to organize his family's return to the plantation.

Meriwether managed the plantation for a time but felt dissatisfied. He missed the frontier life and yearned for adventure. In 1794, Lewis joined the Virginia militia and soon afterward transferred to the United States Army.

In 1795, Lewis served in a rifle company under Captain William Clark. Though they served together for only six months, each sensed that the other could be trusted completely, and they formed a friendship. Lewis would serve as a soldier for six years. He advanced to captain but never saw battle.

When Thomas Jefferson became president, he chose Lewis as his personal secretary. Jefferson valued knowledge and discovery. He and Lewis shared a fascination with nature. As the president's secretary, Lewis took opportunities to further his own education in science, literature, history, and geography.

Jefferson asked Lewis to lead an expedition to try to cross the continent to the Pacific Ocean. Careful planning was required. Lewis spent two years making detailed arrangements. He learned new skills, such as star navigation, and organized supplies.

Lewis made decisions about the kind of men who would work together well on a long, difficult journey. He wanted physically strong woodsmen, capable of hunting for their own food. He hoped to find men with specialized skills, too, such as blacksmithing and interpreting Native American languages.

This would be a military expedition, and Lewis would lead it as captain. But he needed another officer with proven leadership ability who would share responsibility and take over in the case of his own death. He wrote to his friend William Clark, who was now running a farm in Indiana.

Lewis described the mission in detail: river travel up the Missouri to see whether a water route might be found all the way to the western ocean. He wrote about the preparations he had made and the dangers and honors ahead. He wrote, "Believe me there is no man on Earth with whom I should feel equal pleasure in sharing them as with yourself." He offered the job of cocaptain to William Clark. When Clark accepted, their famous partnership began.

**12** Read the paragraph from the text. Underline **two** words that **best** explain why Lewis asked Clark to join him as cocaptain.

In 1795, Lewis served in a rifle company under Captain William Clark. Though they served together for only six months, each sensed that the other could be trusted completely, and they formed a friendship. Lewis would serve as a soldier for six years. He advanced to captain but never saw battle.

**13** What text structure is used to organize the text?

Ⓐ cause and effect

Ⓑ chronological order

Ⓒ problem and solution

Ⓓ compare and contrast

**14** Select the **two** statements that **best** describe the ways in which Thomas Jefferson and Meriwether Lewis are similar.

Ⓐ Both led a cross-country expedition.

Ⓑ Both managed a plantation.

Ⓒ Both are capable hunters.

Ⓓ Both appreciate nature.

Ⓔ Both value discovery.

**15** Read the sentence from the text.

Meriwether managed the plantation for a time but felt <u>dissatisfied</u>.

What is the **best** definition of <u>dissatisfied</u>?

Ⓐ tired

Ⓑ content

Ⓒ not happy

Ⓓ overworked

Name _____ Date _____

**Read the text. Then answer the questions.**

# Stone Soup

There once was a man who had been traveling throughout the countryside for many years. He was exhausted and hungry, so he decided to stop in a village for rest and refreshment. When the villagers saw him, they hurried to put away their food. They were selfish people, and they did not want to share their provisions with strangers.

The traveler decided to teach them a valuable lesson. He went to the middle of the village square and put down his pack. He took out a shiny black soup pot, a big spoon, and a sharp knife. He filled the pot with water, built a fire, and set the pot on the fire. Soon the water in the pot was bubbling furiously as the villagers peeked curiously out of their windows. They watched the traveler pick up a handful of small stones and drop them into the steaming water, stirring and stirring all the while.

One of the village women walked over to the traveler and asked, "What are you making in that pot, my good man?"

"I'm making stone soup," the traveler replied. "It is almost done, and it's very delicious! Now if only I had one carrot, the flavor would be just perfect."

"I have one carrot," the woman said, and she bolted home to get it. She returned with the delightful, bright orange vegetable. The traveler cut the carrot into small pieces and added them to the pot.

In a few minutes, a man came out of his cottage to see what was happening. "What's in the pot?" he asked the traveler.

"I am making stone soup," the traveler explained. "It is almost ready, but if only I had one onion, how much better my soup would be!"

"I have one onion," said the man, and he went back to his house, returning with a very large onion. The traveler cut the onion into slices and dropped the slices into the bubbling pot.

Soon a small circle of curious observers had gathered around the traveler and his pot of stone soup. Occasionally, the traveler would remember another thing that would add more flavor to his soup, and he would ask the fascinated and now starving villagers for the necessary ingredient. For example, he would say, "If only I had some potatoes!" Almost immediately, one of the villagers would run home to fetch some. Then the traveler would say, "If only I had some tasty green beans." As fast as lightning, another villager would get him some. Then he said, "A few beets and a clove of garlic would really improve my soup." Presto! Beets and a clove of garlic would appear and be added to the pot.

As the villagers pooled their resources, the pot continued to fill up with all sorts of ingredients. Finally, the traveler said, "If only I had some salt and spices!" Villagers then scurried home to fetch salt, pepper, thyme, and other herbs and spices.

Soon everyone in the village had gathered in the square to watch the strange traveler stir his concoction, as a delicious aroma wafted through the air. "It's done!" cried the traveler happily. He filled a mug with the steaming liquid and offered the rest of the soup to the villagers. Each villager thoroughly enjoyed the soup, and they all unanimously agreed that it was a miracle that soup made out of stones could taste so extraordinarily delicious.

Name _____ Date _____

**16** Read the paragraph from the text.

As the villagers pooled their resources, the pot continued to fill up with all sorts of ingredients. Finally, the traveler said, "If only I had some salt and spices!" Villagers then <u>scurried</u> home to fetch salt, pepper, thyme, and other herbs and spices.

What is the **best** definition of <u>scurried</u> as used in this paragraph?

Ⓐ rushed

Ⓑ skipped

Ⓒ strolled

Ⓓ walked

**17** Choose **two** ways in which the villagers and the traveler were different.

Ⓐ The villagers had food, but the traveler didn't.

Ⓑ The villagers were happy, but the traveler wasn't.

Ⓒ The villagers were selfish, but the traveler wasn't.

Ⓓ The villagers were hungry, but the traveler wasn't.

Ⓔ The villagers shared their food, but the traveler didn't.

**18** Read the dictionary definition below.

pool/puːl/ *noun* **1.** a body of still water **2.** a location for swimming *verb* **3.** to put into together for use by all **4.** to cause liquid to collect

Read the sentence from the text.

As the villagers <u>pooled</u> their resources, the pot continued to fill up with all sorts of ingredients.

Which meaning **best** fits the way the word <u>pooled</u> is used in the sentence?

Ⓐ meaning 1

Ⓑ meaning 2

Ⓒ meaning 3

Ⓓ meaning 4

19   This question has two parts. First, answer part A. Then, answer part B.

**Part A**

Which conclusion is supported by the text?

  Ⓐ   The traveler has been to the village before.

  Ⓑ   The traveler does not want to share his soup.

  Ⓒ   The villagers change from selfish to generous.

  Ⓓ   The villagers want the traveler to ask for their food.

**Part B**

Select **two** details from the text that support the answer in part A.

  Ⓐ   When the villagers saw him, they hurried to put away their food.

  Ⓑ   He went to the middle of the village square and put down his pack.

  Ⓒ   He filled a mug with the steaming liquid and offered the rest of the soup to the villagers.

  Ⓓ   Villagers then scurried home to fetch salt, pepper, thyme, and other herbs and spices.

  Ⓔ   Soon a small circle of curious observers had gathered around the traveler and his pot of stone soup.

Name _____ Date _____

**20** This question has two parts. First, answer part A. Then, answer part B.

**Part A**

The text is told from what point of view?

Ⓐ  first person

Ⓑ  second person

Ⓒ  third person limited

Ⓓ  third person omniscient

**Part B**

Read the paragraphs below and underline **three** sentences that support the answer to part A.

There once was a man who had been traveling throughout the countryside for many years. He was exhausted and hungry, so he decided to stop in a village for rest and refreshment. When the villagers saw him, they hurried to put away their food. They were selfish people, and they did not want to share their provisions with strangers.

The traveler decided to teach them a valuable lesson. He went to the middle of the village square and put down his pack. He took out a shiny black soup pot, a big spoon, and a sharp knife. He filled the pot with water, built a fire, and set the pot on the fire. Soon the water in the pot was bubbling furiously as the villagers peeked curiously out of their windows. They watched the traveler pick up a handful of small stones and drop them into the steaming water, stirring and stirring all the while.

# Writing

**Read and answer each question.**

**21** Mia is writing a story for her class about a basketball tournament. She wants to edit to eliminate any misspelled words. Read the paragraph and underline the **two** words that have spelling errors.

> My team played hard, but each victory was a struggel. During the final game, I nearly caused my team to lose the tournament. The referee watched carefully as I took a stumble, ready to blow his whistel if I stepped out of bounds. Luckily I stayed inside the line, and we won the trophy.

**22** Which of the following sentences has an error in punctuation?

Ⓐ "Look, you woke the baby"! Jasper exclaimed.

Ⓑ She said, "Ana will enjoy the cake you baked for her."

Ⓒ "My family enjoyed a picnic lunch at the park," Aaron said.

Ⓓ June explained, "Kylie and her family are traveling to Mount Rushmore."

**23** Choose the sentence that contains a spelling error.

Ⓐ She is our new mayer.

Ⓑ Use the sponge to absorb the liquid.

Ⓒ Lexi is a volunteer at the animal shelter.

Ⓓ The long wait to ride the roller coaster was worthwhile.

Name _____ Date _____

**24** Omar is writing an essay for his class about the White House. Read the draft of his first paragraph and complete the task that follows.

> The White House is located in Washington, DC. It is the home of our nation's president. The White House is an important symbol of the U.S. presidency. It has seen a wide range of occupants. It has hosted visitors from all over the world. The history of the White House even explains how Washington, DC, became our nation's capital.

The first sentence of the essay is not the best choice. Which sentence should be moved to the beginning of this paragraph?

Ⓐ   It is the home for our nation's president.

Ⓑ   The White House is an important symbol of the U.S. presidency.

Ⓒ   It has seen a wide range of occupants.

Ⓓ   The history of the White House even explains how Washington, DC, became our nation's capital.

**25** What is the direct object in this sentence?

> My friend Braedon handed me a pencil.

Ⓐ   me

Ⓑ   friend

Ⓒ   pencil

Ⓓ   Braedon

**26** Ariana wrote a letter to her principal. Read a passage from her letter. Underline **three** words that could be improved in order to elaborate on Ariana's opinion.

> Our current marching uniforms are faded and need repair. We practice our routine and have our music memorized. We just don't look as nice as other bands.

**27**   Josiah wrote an essay to inform his class about how to make a wooden derby car. Read the paragraph from his essay and complete the task that follows.

> The most important step to building a wooden derby car is creating the design. Take a sheet of paper and draw the outline of your derby car. <u>A simple shape can be used.</u> Then cut out the outline of your derby car, and tape it to your block of wood to use as a template. Ask an adult to help you cut your block of wood according to your design.

How can the underlined sentence be revised to better explain the topic?

Ⓐ   A simple wedge shape can be used to make a super-fast car.

Ⓑ   A simple shape can be used to make your derby car.

Ⓒ   A basic shape can be used to make a super-fast car.

Ⓓ   A simple design can be used to make your derby car.

**28**   Which sentence uses a verb that is in the past tense?

Ⓐ   She walked to the gym to play basketball.

Ⓑ   Phoebe is pleased to attend your performance.

Ⓒ   I will travel to New Mexico for vacation.

Ⓓ   I am going to finish the task before the end of the week.

Name _____ Date _____

**29** Michael wrote a report about Florida panthers. Read the paragraph from his report, and think about the changes he could make.

> The creatures known as Florida panthers are actually cougars. Their habitats have been drastically reduced since Florida became a state in 1845. About one-third of the forest in Florida was cleared as people built homes and communities.

Which **two** sentences could be the conclusion of this paragraph?

Ⓐ Tracking the panthers helped scientists learn about the health of the remaining panthers.

Ⓑ The Florida panther was put on the endangered species list.

Ⓒ It wasn't long before the only panthers lived in the southern tip of the state.

Ⓓ It seemed likely that the Florida panther would become extinct.

Ⓔ The panther is doing well in Florida.

**30** Cecilia is writing about her summer vacation. Read the draft of her story and complete the task that follows.

> My family took a summer vacation. We drove to California to visit my uncle. Along the way we stopped at the Grand Canyon and hiked. We had an adventure!

Rewrite the paragraph to add more detail. Be sure to include vivid details and sensory words.

_____

_____

_____

_____

_____

Name _____ Date _____

# Listening

**Listen to the presentation. Then answer the questions.**

# Cougars in North America

Name _____ Date _____

**31** What is the main idea of this presentation?

Ⓐ Little is known about how cougars survive.

Ⓑ North America is home to a big cat called the cougar.

Ⓒ To survive, cougars need food, places to hide, and a lot of space.

Ⓓ Cougars need hilly terrain to stalk their prey.

**32** Select the supporting evidence that **best** supports each idea from the presentation.

| | Supporting Evidence A: A cougar crouches low to follow a deer. | Supporting Evidence B: Cougars stalk their prey. | Supporting Evidence C: Every cougar has a home range. |
|---|---|---|---|
| **Idea 1:** Cougars need places to hide. | | | |
| **Idea 2:** Cougars need a lot of space. | | | |

**33** Which detail from the presentation **best** supports the idea cougars need a lot of space?

Ⓐ Cougars need places, such as plants and bushes, to stalk their prey.

Ⓑ Scientists have determined three things cougars need in their habitats.

Ⓒ A hilly, rocky terrain can also provide many hiding places for cougars.

Ⓓ One male cougar's territory can be anywhere from 25 to 500 square miles.

Name _____ Date _____

## Listen to the presentation. Then answer the questions.

# Water Buffalo

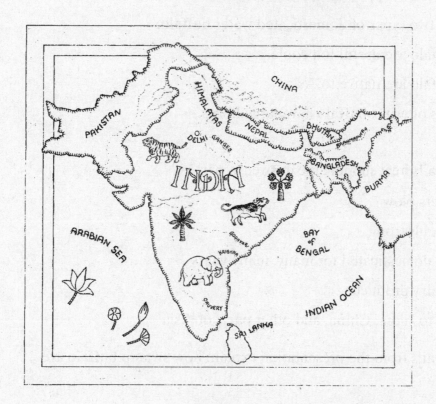

Name _____ Date _____

**34** This question has two parts. First, answer part A. Then, answer part B.

**Part A**

Which conclusion is supported by the presentation?

Ⓐ   There are two types of domesticated water buffalo.

Ⓑ   Water buffalo are useful to people.

Ⓒ   Water buffalo are native to Asia.

Ⓓ   Both types of water buffalo have large horns.

**Part B**

Which **two** details **best** support the answer in part A?

Ⓐ   help farmers plow

Ⓑ   are large and strong

Ⓒ   have been domesticated for many, many years

Ⓓ   provide dairy products

Ⓔ   are native to India, China, and other parts of Asia

**35** Which **two** details from the presentation explain how swamp buffalo are useful?

Ⓐ   provide the milk used to make ghee

Ⓑ   pull heavy plows in rice fields

Ⓒ   may be used for food if injured

Ⓓ   weigh 3,200 pounds

Ⓔ   horns droop

**36** Which idea in the presentation **best** supports the statement that people in India, Pakistan, and Egypt cook with a butter made from buffalo milk?

Ⓐ   Ghee is a food made from buffalo milk.

Ⓑ   Water buffalo are important work animals.

Ⓒ   Rice is an important crop in southern China.

Ⓓ   River buffalo are an important source of milk.

Name _____ Date _____

**Listen to the presentation. Then answer the questions.**

# Brainy Bottlenoses

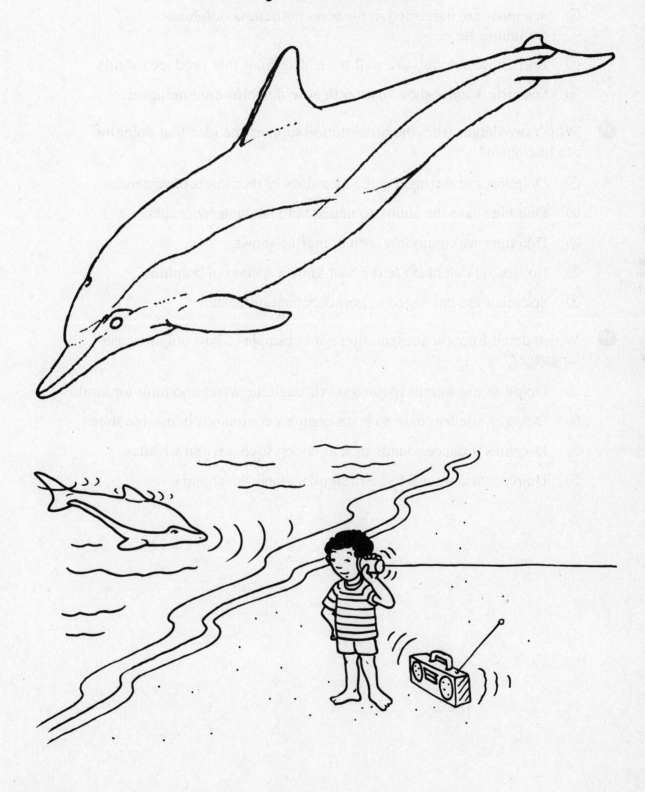

Name _____ Date _____

**37** What does the author hope the listener will learn from the presentation?

(A) A study of one bottlenose dolphin showed these animals understand language concepts.

(B) Scientists are interested in the ways bottlenose dolphins communicate.

(C) Bottlenose dolphins are well-trained animals that produce sounds.

(D) Scientific studies show that bottlenose dolphins are intelligent.

**38** Which **two** details from the presentation support the idea that dolphins are intelligent?

(A) Dolphins can distinguish the meanings of thousands of sentences.

(B) Dolphins have the ability to understand language concepts.

(C) Dolphins are commonly seen in marine shows.

(D) Bottlenose dolphins are the best-known species of dolphins.

(E) Scientists are interested in how they communicate.

**39** Which detail from the presentation is an example of how dolphins use language?

(A) Dolphins use sounds to navigate through the water and hunt for food.

(B) Dolphins use language to learn complex commands in marine shows.

(C) Dolphins produce sounds such as clicks, squeaks, and whistles.

(D) Dolphins use sounds to learn sign-language vocabulary.

# Research

**Read and answer each question.**

**40** A student is writing a research report about technology in the classroom. She wrote the following opinion: "Students should be able to use cell phones in class for educational purposes." She found a source. Read the source and underline the **two** sentences that **support** the opinion.

> Some schools do not allow students to use their cell phones during class. Teachers think that students will use the cell phone to talk to their friends. However, cell phones with access to the Internet can be used like a computer. Students can look up the meanings of confusing words. They can even use their phones to take pictures of notes on the board.

**41** A student is writing a research report about the use of cell phones in the classroom. He wrote the following opinion: "Students should be able to use cell phones in class for educational purposes." He found a source. Read the source and underline the sentence that **opposes** his opinion.

> Many students use cell phones to talk with parents and friends. Students often take their cell phones to school. This allows them to reach parents when needed. Unfortunately, cell phones can be a problem if used in class. Students may use cell phones to send messages to friends or play games instead of working.

Name _____ Date _____

 **42** A student is creating a calendar of local events in his community. He looks in the events section of the newspaper for ideas and finds the following article. Read it and answer the question below.

> Come visit over 100 booths at the Jefferson Arts Center's Annual Spring Craft Fair. Artists from the community will be selling many handmade crafts ranging from candles and soap to teddy bears. Also check out beautiful wood carvings and jewelry. Kids can enjoy face painting and a puppet show. The fair is open all week from 10 a.m. until 4 p.m. Don't miss it!

Select the **two** statements that **best** describe the author's purpose in writing this article.

Ⓐ   to organize craft fair exhibitors

Ⓑ   to offer a different point of view

Ⓒ   to offer step-by-step instructions

Ⓓ   to inform readers about an event

Ⓔ   to persuade readers to do something

Ⓕ   to determine whether or not the fair was successful

Name _____     Date _____

**43**  A student is writing a report about proper equipment and bicycle safety. He found this chart. Read the chart and the directions that follow.

**Bicycle Helmet Size Guide**

| Junior | Centimeters | Inches |
|--------|-------------|--------|
| Small | 48–50 cm | 19–19.7 in. |
| Medium | 51–53 cm | 20–20.8 in. |
| Large | 54–56 cm | 21–22 in. |

The student found a second source. Read the second source.

> Before riding, always be sure that your bicycle is working properly. Inspect the breaks and tires, and wear a proper-fitting helmet. Whether riding during the day or at night, be sure to wear bright reflective clothing so that others can see you. While riding, watch out for people, objects, and animals on the road. Paths just for bicycles are safer than riding on the road. Avoid riding on roads with parked cars.

Which detail from the second source supports the information in the chart?

Ⓐ  Before riding, always be sure that your bicycle is working properly.

Ⓑ  Inspect the breaks and tires, and wear a proper-fitting helmet.

Ⓒ  Whether riding during the day or at night, be sure to wear bright reflective clothing so that others can see you.

Ⓓ  While riding, watch out for people, objects, and animals on the road.

Name _____ Date _____

**44** Read the following source and answer the question.

Before riding, always be sure that your bicycle is working properly. Inspect the breaks and tires, and wear a proper-fitting helmet. Whether riding during the day or at night, be sure to wear bright reflective clothing so that others can see you. While riding, watch out for people, objects, and animals on the road. Paths just for bicycles are safer than riding on the road. Avoid riding on roads with parked cars. Also, pay attention to weather conditions.

What **three** conclusions can a student draw after reading the source?

Ⓐ As long as you wear reflective clothing, it is safe to ride at night.

Ⓑ As long as you pay attention to the weather, you should be able to ride your bicycle safely.

Ⓒ To stay safe, prepare yourself and your equipment and pay attention while you ride.

Ⓓ To protect yourself, be sure that other people can see you.

Ⓔ Safe bicyclists take care of their equipment.

Ⓕ Safe bicyclists trust that other people and drivers will look out for them.

# Performance Task 2

## Part 1

# Life in the Old West

**Task**

Your class recently took a trip to a local museum, where you learned about the early pioneers in your area. This has made you interested in learning more about life in the Old West. You have found three sources about this topic in the school library.

After you have reviewed these sources, you will answer some questions about them. Briefly scan the sources and the three questions that follow. Then, go back and read the sources carefully so you will have the information you will need to answer the questions and complete your research. You may use scratch paper to take notes on the information you find in the sources as you read.

In Part 2, you will write an opinion paper using information you have read.

**Directions for Beginning**

You will now review several sources. You can review any of the sources as often as you like.

**Research Questions**

After reviewing the research sources, use the rest of the time in Part 1 to answer three questions about them. Your answers to these questions will be scored. Also, your answers will help you think about the information you have read, which should help you write your opinion paper.

You may refer back to your scratch paper to review your notes when you think it would be helpful. Answer the questions in the spaces below the items.

Your written notes on scratch paper will be available to you in Part 1 and Part 2 of the performance task.

Name _____ Date _____

# Part 1

**Source #1**
You have found an article that describes the events leading up to the California Gold Rush and the men who traveled in search of fortune.

# Gold!

James Marshall made an amazing discovery in 1848 that would forever change the life of thousands of Americans: gold.

On January 24, 1848, Marshall, a carpenter from New Jersey, was working to build a sawmill for John Sutter. Sutter was a pioneer who set up industries on the frontier of California. While building, Marshall discovered flakes of gold in the riverbed. The men tried to keep their discovery a secret, but word soon spread.

Within months, tiny samples of gold were on display for prospectors to see. Some people included samples of gold in letters they sent to friends and family. Stories were soon exaggerated. Some stories claimed that miners were able to easily dig barrels full of gold. Excitement spread all over the country.

Soon thousands of fortune seekers were traveling to northern California in hopes of striking it rich. These prospectors were often men who were called "Forty-Niners." They were named for the year they traveled to California. They traveled hundreds or even thousands of miles. They crossed rivers, mountains, deserts, and even oceans. Many of these men had little prospect of wealth in the East. They left behind families, farms, and jobs to make a quick fortune. They gave little thought to the perils they might face, but they risked being alone in a new place, being injured while searching for gold, or getting lost in the wilderness.

Some miners were lucky enough to find valuable nuggets. Many men could make a month's wages in only one day of mining. Men who did not find their riches in the goldfield often became entrepreneurs. They started businesses that sold a variety of goods needed by the miners.

By 1850, much of the surface gold was gone. Miners struggled as gold became more difficult to find. Men still journeyed to California, but they were not likely to strike it rich.

**Source #2**
You have found an article that describes the history of the Santa Fe Trail.

# The Santa Fe Trail

During the 1800s, thousands of people traveled cross-country along the Santa Fe Trail. The trail stretched from Independence, Missouri, to Santa Fe, New Mexico. Since the trail crossed the grassy prairie of the Great Plains, many people called it the Great Prairie Highway. For several years, it was the route used by single men and families to make their way across the country.

Travel along the Santa Fe Trail could be difficult and dangerous, but the travelers hoped to make it out west to create a new life and a new home. A one-way wagon trip took about eight weeks. The conditions were usually hot and dusty. Wildfires often raced across the tall prairie grass. Sudden storms would spring up, too. Hail would pelt the canvas covers of the wagons. Heavy rainfall would make the ground muddy and soft.

On a typical day, everyone in a wagon train would wake at dawn, eat, and hitch the oxen to the wagons. The wagons in the train would form two parallel lines. The oxen could pull the wagons quickly into a circle for protection in case there was an attack or emergency. Then the wagon train would set off down the trail.

Name _____ Date _____

The travelers would stop sometime before noon to make repairs to their wagons. They would take care of their animals and eat a meal to keep up their energy. Usually, they would not stop again until dusk. The work didn't end there. The animals would need to be fed and watered. The travelers would have to prepare supper for everyone. Some members of the group would have to stay up during the night to guard the camp.

The American West was expanding rapidly. Many Americans came to believe in an idea called "manifest destiny." This idea stated that American settlers were destined, or meant, to expand across the land now known as the United States until they controlled it from coast to coast. The settlers felt as if they had a right to explore and claim all of the land around them.

This idea caused problems between the United States and Mexico. In the 1840s, Texas declared its independence from Mexico and became a part of the United States. War broke out between the two countries in 1846. There was concern on both sides about access to Santa Fe for trading. Both Americans and Mexicans would lose a lot of money if the Santa Fe Trail were shut down.

The United States was determined to make sure the trade route was not compromised. General Stephen Watts Kearny led soldiers down the Santa Fe Trail. They took Santa Fe without a fight. Soon the United States captured the entire New Mexico territory. This guaranteed that trade and westward expansion would continue.

**Source #3**
You have found an article that describes the life of pioneers who traveled on the Oregon Trail.

# Hitting the Oregon Trail

It was dawn on the prairie. Suddenly, gunshots rang out over the rustling of the long, waving grasses. But this was no gunfight; it was a signal to wake up. Soon, nearly one thousand men, women, and children were awake and moving. Another day on the Oregon Trail had begun.

**78**

Name _____ Date _____

The year was 1843. The people were traveling in a group of 120 covered wagons, called a wagon train. The pioneers trekked along the Oregon Trail all the way from the Missouri River to Oregon. This trip became known as "The Great Migration of 1843." Not many people had attempted the journey over land to the West Coast before. Nonetheless, thousands followed in the years to come. They hoped to begin a new life in the vast wilderness of North America's Far West.

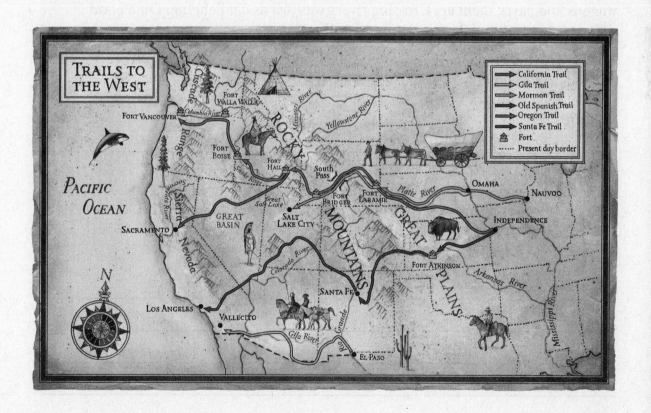

Those who decided to head off on the Oregon Trail had a variety of reasons for making the long, challenging journey. Earlier pioneers had written letters home explaining everything they had discovered. People back east were excited to hear about the rich farmland, the mild weather, and the rivers full of fish. Many were inspired by these accounts.

Another attractive reason to hit the Oregon Trail was the opportunity to start a better life in a new place. Drawn by the promise of free land, many families planned to farm, while other travelers hoped to work as miners, hunters, or loggers. Some intended to open businesses. All kinds of people were needed to settle the rugged lands of the West.

The decision to embark on the journey must have been difficult. Pioneers had to leave relatives and friends behind, knowing that they would probably never see these loved ones again. The trip west was so long and so grueling that it was rare for anyone to return. It was also expensive. For some, it took years to save enough money for supplies, a wagon, and the oxen required to pull it.

Pioneers had to consider the many risks involved in the trip. Many people were injured or died along the way. Others lost all their possessions. Pioneers trekked through scorching deserts and over the tallest mountains. Sometimes the mountains were so steep, people had to unload their belongings from the wagons and carry them up. Crossing rivers was just as challenging. On a good day, a wagon train might travel only 15 or 20 miles.

Today we still remember those who chose to hit the Oregon Trail. Towns and museums all along the route celebrate the history of the trail. They remind people of our country's pioneer heritage.

_____

**1** Source #2 describes problems pioneers faced on a typical day as they traveled to the West. Explain how the information in Source #3 adds to the reader's understanding of how difficult it was to journey west. Give **two** details from Source #3 to support your explanation.

_____

_____

_____

_____

_____

Name _____ Date _____

**2** The sources discuss the benefits and risks that settlers faced as they traveled west. Explain what you have learned about the risks. Use **one** detail from each source to support your explanation.

_____

_____

_____

_____

_____

**3** Mark the boxes to match each source with the idea(s) that it supports. Some ideas may have more than one source selected.

|  | Source #1: Gold ! | Source #2: The Santa Fe Trail | Source #3: Hitting the Oregon Trail |
|---|---|---|---|
| Idea 1: Settlers moved west with dreams of creating a new life. |  |  |  |
| Idea 2: Some travelers seeking fortune in the West became entrepreneurs. |  |  |  |
| Idea 3: Many pioneers believed in manifest destiny. |  |  |  |
| Idea 4: Early settlers dreamed of free farmland and the promise of good weather and endless resources. |  |  |  |

# Part 2

You will now review your notes and sources, and plan, draft, revise, and edit your writing. You may use your notes and go back to the sources. Now read your assignment and the information about how your writing will be scored, and then begin your work.

**Your Assignment:**

Your classmates begin to discuss what they learned about the different difficulties people faced in the Old West. Some students think that the risks pioneers faced were not worth the benefits of traveling to the West, but others believe the benefits of living in the West were worth the difficulties they faced. Your teacher asks you to write a paper explaining your opinion. In your paper, you will take a side as to whether the challenges pioneers had to overcome were worth the payoff once they reached the West.

Your paper will be read by your classmates and your teacher. Make sure you clearly state your opinion and write several paragraphs supporting your opinion with reasons and details from the sources. Develop your ideas clearly and use your own words, except when quoting directly from the sources. Be sure to give the source title or number for the details or facts you use.

**REMEMBER: A well-written opinion paper**

- has a clear opinion.
- is well-organized and stays on the topic.
- has an introduction and conclusion.
- uses transitions.
- uses details from the sources to support your opinion.
- puts the information from the sources in your own words, except when using direct quotations from the sources.
- gives the title or number of the source for the details or facts you included.
- develops ideas clearly.
- uses clear language.
- follows rules of writing (spelling, punctuation, and grammar usage).

Now begin work on your opinion paper. Manage your time carefully so that you can

1. plan your opinion paper.
2. write your opinion paper.
3. revise and edit the final draft of your opinion paper.

Name _____ Date _____

For Part 2, you are being asked to write an opinion paper that is several paragraphs long. Write your response in the space below.

Remember to check your notes and your prewriting and planning as you write, and then revise and edit your opinion paper.

_____

_____

_____

_____

_____

_____

_____

_____

_____

_____

_____

_____

_____

_____

_____

_____

_____

_____

_____

_____

_____

_____

_____

Name _____ Date _____

Name _____ Date _____

_____

_____

_____

_____

_____

_____

_____

_____

_____

_____

_____

_____

_____

_____

_____

_____

_____

_____

_____

_____

_____

_____

_____

_____

_____

# Assessment 3
## Reading

Read the text. Then answer the questions.

# Two Hundred Tries

Rosa kicked the skateboard with full force, sending it skidding across the garage. She had to face the facts. Her idea for an invention was a complete and utter failure. She'd wanted to make a skateboard with wheels arranged in a single row, so that the rider could tilt from side to side on it. She imagined how it would glide smoothly with nimble motions and quick turns and how jealous her boarding friends would be when they saw her new invention. Now she'd ended up with a mess. It was a total train wreck!

Rosa had been working on her invention for about two weeks. First, she had persuaded her sister Paz to give her a skateboard that she rarely used, and then Rosa took off its wheels, so she could replace them with wheels in a straight row. Next, after a lot of searching, she tracked down an ancient pair of skates with wheels arranged in one row. The skates had removable wheels, and she planned to take them off one of the skates and attach them to her board in what seemed like a simple process. However, this was much more difficult than it had first appeared because there was no way to fasten the wheels to the board with screws or nails. Instead, she had used glue, and that, to put it mildly, didn't work out well at all. Each time she tested the board, it would fall over before she had gone two feet. Then the wheels would come unstuck, so she'd have to glue them back on. And she still didn't have the slightest idea how she was going to make the board tilt.

"I quit!" Rosa yelled.

"Hey, what's all the shouting about?" her father asked as he stepped into the garage.

"I don't know why I thought I could invent something because obviously I can't," Rosa said.

"Have you ever heard of the Wright brothers?" asked her dad.

"Aren't they the guys who made the airplane?" Rosa answered, wondering where this conversation was headed.

"Yes," said her dad, "and guess how many designs they tried for the wings of their plane?"

Name _____ Date _____

"Twenty?" said Rosa.

"No, they tried about 200 designs before they found one that worked. And how many skateboard designs have you tried?"

"One," Rosa murmured.

Dad continued, "The Wright brothers started with an idea just like you have. They thought about how they could use what they knew about bicycles and somehow make something that could fly. And guess what? Their first ideas didn't work very well; in fact, when the Wright brothers tested out their designs, they brought along spare parts because they planned on some serious crashes. They knew their ideas wouldn't work the first time."

She suddenly felt a little sheepish.

"Are you still ready to give up?" her dad asked. Rosa threw her hands into the air and sighed loudly.

"This invention process can be pretty frustrating, Dad."

"Maybe you should try something other than glue," said her dad. Rosa looked around the garage and noticed a roll of strong duct tape on a hook beside a shelf. She got an idea: Maybe she could try taping the wheels onto the board.

"Dad, I think you're right," she said with a hint of a grin. "I'll try something new."

"Go for it!" her dad said. "And when that doesn't work, try a third new thing. Then a fourth. I'll bet that somewhere along the line, you'll get a design that does just what you want it to do."

**1** Read the sentences from the text.

"Their first ideas didn't work very well; in fact, when the Wright brothers tested out their designs, they brought along spare parts because they planned on some serious crashes. They knew their ideas wouldn't work the first time."

She suddenly felt a little sheepish.

What information from Rosa's father would have caused Rosa to feel "a little sheepish"?

Ⓐ Rosa's father knows a lot of history.

Ⓑ Rosa's father tells about planning for crashes.

Ⓒ Rosa's father gives her ideas about new designs.

Ⓓ Rosa's father tells how others have shown more effort than she has shown.

**2** In what sequence does Rosa complete these actions? Label the events from the text in the order in which they happen. The first event will be labeled 1, and the last event will be labeled 5.

_____ Rosa attaches skate wheels.

_____ Rosa finds an old pair of skates.

_____ Rosa gets a skateboard.

_____ Rosa tests the skateboard.

_____ Rosa kicks the skateboard.

**3** Read the paragraph from the text. Underline **three** words that the author uses to show the point of the view.

Rosa kicked the skateboard with full force, sending it skidding across the garage. She had to face the facts. Her idea for an invention was a complete and utter failure.

Name _____    Date _____

**4**   This question has two parts. First, answer part A. Then, answer part B.

**Part A**

How is Rosa's problem resolved at the end of the text?

Ⓐ   Her father teaches her to think about other designs.

Ⓑ   Rosa gives up on her idea of inventing a new skateboard.

Ⓒ   Rosa figures out a way to screw a row of wheels onto the skateboard.

Ⓓ   Her father fixes her new invention by taping the wheels on the skateboard.

**Part B**

Select the sentence from the text that **best** supports the answer to part A.

Ⓐ   "Have you ever heard of the Wright brothers?" asked her dad.

Ⓑ   "Aren't they the guys who made the airplane?" Rosa answered, wondering where this conversation was headed.

Ⓒ   "Yes," said her dad, "and guess how many designs they tried for the wings of their plane?"

Ⓓ   "No, they tried about 200 designs before they found one that worked."

**5** This question has two parts. First, answer part A. Then, answer part B.

**Part A**

What is Rosa's biggest problem in the text?

Ⓐ Her ideas don't work.

Ⓑ She gives up too easily.

Ⓒ She won't follow directions.

Ⓓ Her father disagrees with her.

**Part B**

Select the sentence from the text that **best** supports the answer to part A.

Ⓐ Each time she tested the board, it would fall over before she had gone two feet. Then the wheels would come unstuck, so she'd have to glue them back on.

Ⓑ And she still didn't have the slightest idea how she was going to make the board tilt.

Ⓒ "I don't know why I thought I could invent something because obviously I can't," Rosa said.

Ⓓ "Maybe you should try something other than glue," said her dad.

**Read the text. Then answer the questions.**

# Mateo's Big Idea

I was riding the bus with my mother, going downtown to shop for a new winter jacket. When we stopped for a red light, I noticed a small group of men sitting on benches in Hancock Park whose clothes appeared to be old and torn. There were dirty blankets and some overstuffed plastic trash bags scattered on the grass around the benches.

I asked, "Mom, do those people actually live in the park? Do they sleep there?"

My mother said, "Sometimes, Mateo, they might sleep outside in the park. They might sleep in shelters where they can get something to eat, too."

Throughout the afternoon, I thought about those homeless people, wondering, had they always been there, and I just hadn't seen them?

The image of the men in the park weighed on my mind, so I talked it over with Franca, a friend in my class. Franca has often volunteered to help people in the community, and she has even tried to get me involved.

"It must get freezing out there in the park," I said.

"It certainly does," she nodded. "Some of those people don't even have winter coats."

"Maybe we could organize a clothing drive at school, where we could probably collect a lot of stuff," I said.

She replied, "You know, Mateo, you're starting to sound like me. That's an awesome idea!"

It took Franca and me a week to figure out a workable plan, which we shared with my mother. We explained how the system would work and the various ways we would encourage people to bring donations of winter clothing to the school.

Mom said, "This is quite an impressive project, you two." Then she asked me gently, "Are you ready to get up and talk to the whole school, Mateo? You've always been shy about speaking in front of a group. Maybe Franca should do the talking?"

Franca protested, "But this was Mateo's idea! I'll stand up there with you, Mateo, for support, but you should speak. Otherwise, it will look like me doing my volunteer thing again."

Mom agreed with her, and after some convincing, I grudgingly agreed.

Franca and I presented the idea to our principal the next morning, and she gave us her enthusiastic approval. Then we arranged an assembly to announce the clothing drive to the entire school.

At the assembly, the principal introduced me. When I began to speak, the thumping of my heart became so deafening that I could barely hear my own voice. I kept talking, though, and when I finished, everyone applauded. Franca even high-fived me. It's strange, but afterward, I felt different, like I'd suddenly gotten a little taller, or a little stronger, or a little better.

After that, it was easy to coordinate the clothing drive with the representatives of the homeless shelter. For three weekends, we collected items in the school gymnasium, and soon it started to resemble a warehouse. Throughout the effort, I discovered that I was more outgoing, and I was less fearful of speaking up or of taking charge of a situation.

On the final day, the shelter staff packed the last carton of clothing into a van. Then the shelter's director took me aside. "Thanks to you, Mateo, we have more warm clothing. We'll be able to distribute it to people who really need it." She added appreciatively, "You've made a tremendous difference in these people's lives."

When I thought over the whole experience later, I felt a big grin spreading across my face. Yes, my efforts had made a difference for others, but I was also surprised and happy to learn they had made a difference in me, too.

Name _____ Date _____

**6** Read the sentences from the text.

> At the assembly, the principal introduced me. When I began to speak, the thumping of my heart became so deafening that I could barely hear my own voice. I kept talking, though, and when I finished, everyone applauded.

What is the meaning of the words "the thumping of my heart became so deafening that I could barely hear my own voice"?

Ⓐ Mateo is nervous.

Ⓑ The room is very loud.

Ⓒ Mateo is having heart problems.

Ⓓ Mateo is having trouble hearing.

**7** Read the sentences from the text.

> I was riding the bus with my mother, going downtown to shop for a new winter jacket. When we stopped for a red light, I noticed a small group of men sitting on benches in Hancock Park whose clothes appeared to be old and torn. There were dirty blankets and some overstuffed plastic trash bags scattered on the grass around the benches.
>
> I asked, "Mom, do those people actually live in the park? Do they sleep there?"
>
> My mother said, "Sometimes, Mateo, they might sleep outside in the park. They might sleep in shelters where they can get something to eat, too."
>
> Throughout the afternoon, I thought about those homeless people, wondering, had they always been there, and I just hadn't seen them?

What are **three** details that **most likely** cause Mateo to organize a coat drive?

Ⓐ The season was winter.

Ⓑ Mateo was riding a bus.

Ⓒ The men's clothing was old and torn.

Ⓓ Shelters offer food and a place to sleep.

Ⓔ The men sometimes sleep in the cold park.

**8** Read the sentences from the text.

> Mom said, "This is quite an impressive project, you two." Then she asked me gently, "Are you ready to get up and talk to the whole school, Mateo? You've always been shy about speaking in front of a group. Maybe Franca should do the talking?"

Why does the author have Mateo's mom say, "Maybe Franca should do the talking?"

Ⓐ to show that Franca is a better speaker

Ⓑ to show that Mom has little confidence in Mateo

Ⓒ to show that Mom wants Mateo to be comfortable

Ⓓ to show that Mateo is too young to speak to an audience

**9** One of the themes in the text deals with the way people can grow and change when they encounter difficult challenges. Support this theme with **two** details from the text.

_____

_____

_____

_____

**10** Read the sentence and the directions that follow.

> When you help others, you may also help yourself.

Underline the **two** sentences that **best** support this theme of the text.

> On the final day, the shelter staff packed the last carton of clothing into a van. Then the shelter's director took me aside. "Thanks to you, Mateo, we have more warm clothing. We'll be able to distribute it to people who really need it." She added appreciatively, "You've made a tremendous difference in these people's lives."

> When I thought over the whole experience later, I felt a big grin spreading across my face. Yes, my efforts had made a difference for others, but I was also surprised and happy to learn they had made a difference in me, too.

Name _____ Date _____

**Read the text. Then answer the questions.**

# The Greatest Adventure

Miguel de Cervantes was born around 1547 near Madrid, Spain. His adventurous life began when he joined the army as a young man. The life of a soldier was perfect for Cervantes since being a soldier meant travel and adventure—and that was what Cervantes wanted. As it happened, he would serve bravely but also suffer hardship.

In 1571, Cervantes and his Spanish regiment fought against the Turks. Spain was victorious, but Cervantes was wounded and spent months in a hospital. By 1575, he was ready to leave the soldier's life, so he set sail for Spain. However, the ship was attacked by pirates. Cervantes was captured and taken to Africa where he spent five difficult years as a prisoner. Cervantes made four attempts to escape. Finally, in 1580, family and friends raised enough money to pay a ransom, which means Cervantes was freed!

Once back in Spain, Cervantes had several jobs. He was a tax collector, a messenger, a purchasing agent, and a government official. He missed his exciting life as a soldier and traveler. However, he used his memories of those experiences as he began to write.

Cervantes wrote stories, plays, and poetry. However, he was not able to earn enough money from his writing. He was even put in prison for debt! Many people believe it was in prison that he got his most brilliant story idea.

That idea was for a novel about a charming but awkward gentleman, Alonso Quixano, who reads books to make his boring life more interesting. Quixano becomes convinced that the tales of knights he reads are true and that he himself is a knight, so he forgets to eat, doesn't sleep, and soon loses his sanity. He finds an old suit of armor, improvises a helmet, and takes a new name.

And so one bright morning, this new and noble knight, Don Quixote de La Mancha, rides off on a quest. He is determined to fight evil, defend the virtuous, and do heroic deeds. And what deeds they are! Don Quixote attacks windmills that he thinks are ferocious giants, and he mistakes a flock of sheep for a great army. He makes an innkeeper the lord of a castle and treats every woman he meets with special courtesy.

*Don Quixote* is a masterpiece published in two volumes. It was the most influential work of literature to emerge from the Spanish Golden Age, which brought Cervantes great fame but not riches.

Translated into more than sixty-five languages, it first appeared in English in 1608. Many people believe that Shakespeare read it. The story has been turned into an opera, a ballet, and a film. In 1965 a musical play adaptation, *Man of La Mancha*, became a huge success.

Cervantes's words painted an amusing picture of the aging Don Quixote and his servant, Sancho. Their adventures are meant to make readers laugh, but Cervantes had a more serious purpose in mind. He used these two characters to tell readers about human nature.

Don Quixote is funny and irritating, but he is also a heroic dreamer who has a noble character and great bravery. He admires all that is good and detests all that is evil. He has all the qualities a reader would want in a hero. His companion, Sancho, is simple and easily led, having blind faith in the hopes and promises of his master. He represents real life for most people of that time.

Cervantes lived a life almost as adventurous and tragic as the life of his hero. He experienced injury, poverty, debt, and prison, but he never lost faith in his own genius, believing that people could be heroes.

---

**11** Which **three** facts support the author's opinion that the novel *Don Quixote* is an influential masterpiece?

&#9398; represented real life for many people

&#9399; features a unique main character

&#9400; translated into many languages

&#9401; turned into a movie

&#9402; made into a musical

Name _____ Date _____

**12** Read the sentence from the text.

> In 1571, Cervantes and his Spanish regiment fought against the Turks.

Now complete the analogy.

An orchestra is to a musician as a regiment is to a _____.

- Ⓐ commander
- Ⓑ weapon
- Ⓒ soldier
- Ⓓ jester

**13** Read the sentences from the text.

> Translated into more than sixty-five languages, it first appeared in English in 1608. Many people believe that Shakespeare read it. The story has been turned into an opera, a ballet, and a film. In 1965 a musical play adaptation, *Man of La Mancha*, became a huge success.

What main idea does the detail about Shakespeare support?

- Ⓐ Cervantes wrote plays.
- Ⓑ The book influenced other writers.
- Ⓒ Cervantes earned his fortune from the book.
- Ⓓ There are few details known about the book.

**14** The author states that Don Quixote "admires all that is good and detests all that is evil." Identify and explain **two** details in the text that support the author's point.

_____

_____

_____

_____

_____

**98**

Name _____ Date _____

**15** This question has two parts. First, answer part A. Then, answer part B.

**Part A**

Read the sentences from the passage.

> Cervantes made four attempts to escape. Finally, in 1580, family
> and friends raised enough money to pay a <u>ransom</u>, which means
> Cervantes was freed!

What does the word <u>ransom</u> mean as it is used in the text?

Ⓐ  price paid to release a prisoner

Ⓑ  punishment for evil deeds

Ⓒ  reward for service

Ⓓ  attack by pirates

**Part B**

Which phrase from the text **best** helps the reader understand the meaning
of the word <u>ransom</u> in part A?

Ⓐ  "made four attempts"

Ⓑ  "family and friends"

Ⓒ  "raised enough money"

Ⓓ  "was freed"

Name _____  Date _____

**Read the text. Then answer the questions.**

# Benjamin Franklin, Young Writer

Benjamin Franklin's life is truly a rags-to-riches story. Franklin was born poor and, through his own hard work, died rich and well respected. From an early age, he used reading, writing, and thinking skills to better his situation. In his autobiography Franklin notes that "prose writing has been of great use to me in the course of my life and was a principal means of my advancement."

Born in Boston in 1706, Ben was the fifteenth of seventeen children. It's not surprising that his father could not afford to send him to school. Ben had only two years of formal schooling, starting at the age of eight. Fortunately, he loved to read, and the rest of his education came from his own studies. At the age of twelve, Ben became an apprentice to his brother James. Ben would learn to be a printer. A few years later, when Ben was about fifteen years old, James began his own newspaper, the *New-England Courant.* Ben helped print and sell the paper.

During those years, Ben continued to read as much as he could. Through his work in the printing shop, he met booksellers and people who owned many books. They were glad to lend books to him, so he borrowed and studied, borrowed and studied. In time he began to imitate the writing style of authors he liked and to summarize their ideas and arguments. He also taught himself to write and speak persuasively.

In 1722, Ben began writing a series of articles in the form of letters to his brother's paper. He thought that his brother would reject the articles if he knew who the author really was, so Ben used the fictional name Silence Dogood. He slipped the letters under the door of the printing shop at night, and his brother published them. These letters, which were humorous, were very popular with the readers. They made fun of Boston society, politics, and religion. Everyone was surprised to find that the author of the letters was really Ben Franklin, who was only sixteen years old!

Differences with his brother caused Ben to move to Philadelphia the next year. He eventually opened his own printing shop, and in 1729 he purchased the newspaper the *Pennsylvania Gazette.* Not only did Ben print the paper, but he also wrote pieces for it. The paper was successful, and Ben used it to suggest new ideas for the colonies.

Name _____ Date _____

In 1732, Ben Franklin published the first edition of an almanac under the name of Richard Saunders. He called it *Poor Richard's Almanack*. The almanac was a calendar full of ads, weather forecasts, recipes, jokes, and sayings. Many familiar sayings that we use today, such as "Haste makes waste" and "A true friend is the best possession," were printed in Franklin's almanac. He published it until 1758.

Many years later, this talented man was called upon to use his skills for more serious purposes. He helped draft the Declaration of Independence and contributed to the U.S. Constitution. Franklin also wrote articles supporting the end of slavery. In his adult life, Ben Franklin became many things, including an author, a politician, a scientist, an inventor, and a diplomat. But he was always a writer.

---

**16**  Read the sentences from the text.

Many familiar sayings that we use today, such as "Haste makes waste" and "A true friend is the best possession," were printed in Franklin's almanac. He published it until 1758.

What is the meaning of the adage "haste makes waste"?

  Ⓐ  Hurrying forces you to make mistakes.

  Ⓑ  Hurrying is always better than wasting time.

  Ⓒ  Getting things done quickly is better than wasting time.

  Ⓓ  Using time wisely can sometimes take longer than you planned.

**17**  Which **four** details support the main idea that Benjamin Franklin was a hard worker?

  Ⓐ  loved to read

  Ⓑ  had many jobs

  Ⓒ  taught himself to write well

  Ⓓ  began working at a young age

  Ⓔ  had differences with his brother

  Ⓕ  owned and wrote for a newspaper

**18** Read the sentences from the text.

> In 1732, Ben Franklin published the first edition of an almanac under the name of Richard Saunders. He called it *Poor Richard's Almanack*. The almanac was a calendar full of ads, weather forecasts, recipes, jokes, and sayings. Many familiar sayings that we use today, such as "Haste makes waste" and "A true friend is the best possession," were printed in Franklin's almanac. He published it until 1758.
>
> Many years later, this talented man was called upon to use his skills for more serious purposes. He helped draft the Declaration of Independence and contributed to the U.S. Constitution. Franklin also wrote articles supporting the end of slavery.

Based on the facts in the text, what opinion does the author **most likely** hold about Franklin's work?

Ⓐ Franklin's adages were his most popular writings.

Ⓑ Franklin's talents were best used for pressing issues.

Ⓒ Writing a newspaper was Franklin's most lasting legacy.

Ⓓ Franklin should have continued publishing *Poor Richard's Almanack*.

**19** Which detail **best** supports the author's point that Ben Franklin "used reading, writing, and thinking skills to better his situation"?

Ⓐ He had two years of formal schooling.

Ⓑ He imitated the writing of his favorite authors.

Ⓒ He made fun of politics in his humorous articles.

Ⓓ He helped to print and sell his brother's newspaper.

Name _____ Date _____

**20** Read the sentences from the text.

> In 1732, Ben Franklin published the first <u>edition</u> of an almanac under the name of Richard Saunders. He called it *Poor Richard's Almanack*.

Which word is a homophone for <u>edition</u>?

- Ⓐ addition
- Ⓑ almanac
- Ⓒ publication
- Ⓓ pseudonym

# Writing

**Read and answer each question.**

**21** A student is revising his story about a personal event. It contains an error in verb usage. Underline the sentence that contains the error.

> He was sure he had done the assignment correctly, so he was shocked that he failed. He hadn't scored so low on an assignment in a long time. By the time he got to the teacher's room after school, she already left. He had hoped to talk to her about it.

**22** A student is editing her book report. It contains spelling errors. Read the paragraph from the book report. Then, underline the word that is spelled incorrectly.

> The inventor arrives in quite an unforgettable way: as people stand talking with one another, a loud noise is heard outside. Surprisingly, these clanks and clatters turn out to be the inventor arriveing in her time machine. The author made an interesting and unusual decision to introduce a character this way!

**23** A student is revising a social studies paper about New Brunswick, Canada. She needs to add details to her paragraph about the plants, animals, and natural formations of New Brunswick. Below are her notes and the first sentence of the paragraph.

Notes:

-not many people (only 700,000 in whole province)

-no true mountains, but hilly

-many rivers—plentiful water to support life

-beautiful forests

-coniferous trees: hemlock, spruce, balsam fir, pine

-deciduous trees: aspen, birch, maple

-other plants: wild blueberries, cranberries

-animals: white-tailed deer, moose, raccoons, porcupines, migratory birds

First sentence: The population of New Brunswick is small—only about 700,000 people—so large areas of its beautiful, hilly forests remain untouched.

Using the notes, write the rest of the paragraph. Write at least **three** sentences. Think about the most effective order in which to present the details.

_____

_____

_____

_____

_____

Name _____ Date _____

**24** A student is editing his essay. It contains spelling errors. Read the paragraph from the essay. Then, read the task that follows.

> My experience at student <u>government</u> camp was a <u>disappointment</u>—but an educational one. Day after day, the seemingly endless debates dragged on. I watched the other campers' faces, so enthusiastic and excited, and I wondered, "Why didn't I feel that way?" One day, I simply couldn't take it any more, so instead, I went for a quiet hike amid the tall pine trees. Everything along the trail was <u>delightfull</u>—the nodding grasses, the brilliant wildflowers. I could have spent weeks exploring the <u>wilderness</u>. When I came back I knew for sure that I'm not going to be a politician after all: I'm going to be a scientist.

Which of the underlined words contains a spelling error?

- Ⓐ disappointment
- Ⓑ government
- Ⓒ delightfull
- Ⓓ wilderness

**25** A student is writing a recipe for bread. It contains the following paragraph.

> (1) First, mix the flour, salt, and baking soda in a large bowl. (2) In another bowl, stir the buttermilk and the egg together. (3) Then, pour the egg mixture into the bowl containing the dry ingredients, and stir until everything is completely mixed. (4) Spread flour on a clean surface and dust flour over your hands.

Which sentence **begins** with a prepositional phrase?

- Ⓐ sentence 1
- Ⓑ sentence 2
- Ⓒ sentence 3
- Ⓓ sentence 4

**26** Which sentence is correct?

Ⓐ When in doubt we always, ask first.

Ⓑ Smiling, she slowly opened the gift.

Ⓒ Down the street, and to the left the library is on the corner.

Ⓓ After walking around the back of the house, and knocking on the door we decided they weren't home.

**27** A student is writing a letter to the editor explaining his opinion about some planned construction. Read the following paragraph of the letter.

> The city's plans for extending Highway 41 through town need to be changed. The plan would require destroying almost 50 buildings and a park along the route. This would mean a huge waste of building materials. Also, these buildings are part of a thriving neighborhood. Tearing them down would harm a stable community that adds to the growth and culture of the city.

Which sentences would **best** fit at the end of this paragraph to conclude the argument?

Ⓐ Highways bring dirt, noise, and pollution wherever they go. This one would be no different.

Ⓑ Why should the highway be extended, anyway? The roads we have are fine. They just need to be repaved, so maybe the city could do that instead.

Ⓒ Last, one of the affected buildings is Foxvale Middle School, whose 2,000 students would all have to go somewhere else. The city's other schools don't have room for that many students.

Ⓓ This area is home to three of the city's ten theaters, two of its three bookstores, and four museums, as well as dozens of other businesses and homes. I urge you to consider a different route for the highway.

Name _____ Date _____

**28** A student is writing a review of a movie for the school paper. This is one paragraph from her review.

> Of the six main characters, only one is a girl: the "brainiac" scientist named Lucy. Although it's good that the filmmakers are showing that girls can be scientists, they don't give Lucy much to do. And as soon as the action really gets started—surprise, surprise—it's always Lucy who gets hurt or kidnapped, and she never gets to fight for herself. She's just rescued by the boys. It shows a disappointing lack of imagination in a film that is otherwise really creative.

Which sentence would be the **most effective** introduction for this paragraph?

Ⓐ Although the movie is enjoyable, it could have been better.

Ⓑ The film centers on a six-person team of oddballs who all have different skills.

Ⓒ Although the movie is enjoyable, it has some problems in the way it shows female characters.

Ⓓ I am so tired of female characters who follow the same damsel-in-distress story over and over again.

Name _____ Date _____

**29** A student is writing an editorial for the school paper. She is arguing in favor of changing the hours of the school day. Read the paragraph from her editorial.

> Changing school hours to 8:30 to 3:30 would have many benefits. With our current starting time of 7:30, many students must wake up as early as 5:00 to catch the bus. Some teachers wake up even earlier to prepare their lessons. At many other schools, activities such as clubs and choir can have meetings or rehearsals before school. That is impossible for us.

Which **two** sentences would further expand this argument?

Ⓐ Nobody likes waking up at 5:00—it just isn't natural.

Ⓑ Most of the students at our school really hate the 7:30–2:30 school day.

Ⓒ Our early start means that in winter, students who walk to school must do so in darkness, which is not safe.

Ⓓ The early end time of our school day creates more problems, especially for students whose parents work.

Ⓔ Another problem is that we never see our school lunch menu in advance, so we don't know which days would be best to bring a sack lunch.

**30** A student is writing a report on the scientist Lise Meitner. Read the paragraph from the report.

> (1) Surprisingly, only two elements in the periodic table, Curium and Meitnerium, are named for women. (2) The female physicist Lise Meitner was born in Vienna, Austria. (3) Because she was Jewish, she fled to Sweden in 1938 to avoid the Nazis. (4) There, she continued her research into radioactivity and fission, and her work would eventually win her the Enrico Fermi Award.

Which sentence should the student remove to improve the paragraph?

Ⓐ sentence 1

Ⓑ sentence 2

Ⓒ sentence 3

Ⓓ sentence 4

# Listening

**Listen to the presentation. Then answer the questions.**

## Saving Leo

**31** Which detail from the presentation **best** supports the idea that the goat herder felt he had to assist Leo?

Ⓐ In Pakistan, they are critically endangered; fewer than three hundred remain.

Ⓑ It was an orphan, and the herder knew it needed help.

Ⓒ Leo became famous in Pakistan, where people hoped that he would find a suitable home.

Ⓓ It was not possible to return Leo to the wild.

**32** How did the specialist Kamal-ud-din help Leo? Choose **two** answers.

Ⓐ He cared for Leo.

Ⓑ He named the cub Leo.

Ⓒ He helped Leo return to the wild.

Ⓓ He created a wildlife center in Pakistan where Leo could live.

Ⓔ He made sure Leo became famous so that people would want to help him.

**33** What is the main idea of this presentation?

Ⓐ Humans must take the responsibility for protecting endangered species such as snow leopards.

Ⓑ Wild animals should never be kept as pets because it is dangerous to both animals and humans.

Ⓒ An orphaned snow leopard has a new life thanks to the help of several people and organizations.

Ⓓ Snow leopards were never meant to live among humans because they need to be raised by their own mothers.

Listen to the presentation. Then answer the questions.

# Nellie Bly, Star Reporter

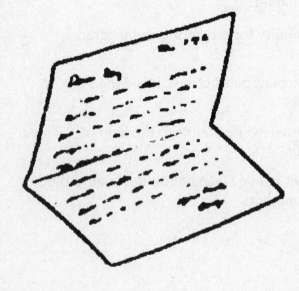

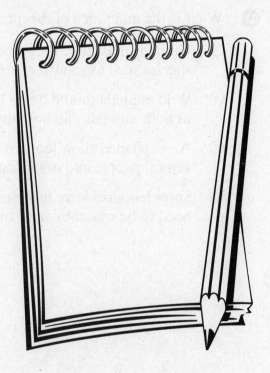

Name _____ Date _____

**34** What is the main idea of the presentation? Select the sentence that **best** states the main idea.

&#9398; Nellie Bly had a career as a reporter partly because of luck.

&#9399; Nellie Bly used her position at the newspaper mostly to fight for the rights of women.

&#9400; Nellie Bly had to change her name and go undercover in order to work at the newspaper.

&#9401; Nellie Bly helped create the field of investigative journalism and proved that women could be reporters.

**35** Which **two** details **best** support the conclusion that Nellie Bly's career was defined by risky actions that broke social rules?

&#9398; writing about child labor

&#9399; going undercover at a mental hospital

&#9400; using a pen name instead of her real name

&#9401; writing for a newspaper in New York City

&#9402; writing an angry letter to the editor of the *Pittsburgh Dispatch*

**36** This question has two parts. First, answer part A. Then, answer part B.

**Part A**

What can you conclude about how the *Pittsburgh Dispatch* treated Nellie Bly immediately after hiring her?

Ⓐ The newspaper made her equal to male reporters.

Ⓑ The newspaper asked her to take risks on investigative stories.

Ⓒ The newspaper told her she should be at home to cook and clean.

Ⓓ The newspaper wanted to limit her writing to topics usually reserved for women.

**Part B**

Which detail from the presentation **best** supports the answer to part A?

Ⓐ In the 1800s, most people, especially men, thought that newspaper work was not fit for women.

Ⓑ In 1880, a columnist for the *Pittsburgh Dispatch* wrote that women should stay home to cook, clean, and sew.

Ⓒ The paper wanted her to write about cooking and fashion, but she preferred to write on topics such as child labor and poverty under the pen name Nellie Bly.

Ⓓ When she moved to New York City to look for reporting jobs, she faced the same challenges.

Name _____ Date _____

**Listen to the presentation. Then answer the questions.**

# Help for Threatened Otters

37 Which detail **best** supports the idea that shipping routes should be moved away from otter habitats?

Ⓐ Otters can get tangled in fishing nets.

Ⓑ Hunters want to kill otters for their dense fur.

Ⓒ Oil that spills from ships can cause otters to die.

Ⓓ Otters do not have a layer of fat to help them stay warm.

38 Read the details from the presentation.

About fifteen thousand sea otters lived off the coast of California before the 1900s.

About one hundred sea otters lived in California waters in the early 1900s.

About three thousand California sea otters exist today.

What is the **most likely** reason the author includes these numbers?

Ⓐ to show that, thanks to conservation efforts, the population of otters is larger than ever

Ⓑ to show that conservation efforts have succeeded in banning otter hunting, but that the ban is unlikely to be effective

Ⓒ to show that, thanks to conservation efforts, the number of sea otters is somewhat larger, but the species is still threatened

Ⓓ to show that conservation efforts have not been happening long enough for their effects on the otter population to be measurable

Name _____ Date _____

**39** The table below contains details from the presentation. Each detail supports one of the key points of the presentation. For each detail, draw an X in the boxes that shows which key point it supports.

| | Facts about Otters | Conservation Efforts |
|---|---|---|
| Eat shellfish and urchins | | |
| Changes to shipping routes | | |
| Dense fur | | |
| Bans on fishing and hunting | | |
| Pollution control | | |

# Research

**Read and answer each question.**

**40** A student is writing a research report about the geology of the Pocono Mountains. Read the sentences from her report.

> The primary rock formation of the Pocono Mountains is sandstone. Its color is primarily gray, and much of the rock faces appear to be formed in thick layers of sand. The mountains have been changed over many centuries as glaciers have moved over the area and scraped away the sharpest peaks of the ancient mountain range.

Select the **two** sources that would **most likely** give the student more information about the ideas she has written.

(A) www.patransit.com

Find bus and train schedules to get to the cities and towns of the Pocono Mountain region.

(B) www.UPenn.edu/geology

Learn what classes you would take at the University of Pennsylvania if you wanted to major in geology.

(C) www.newpoconohomesforsale.com

Look for your Poconos vacation home by browsing the latest real estate listings from north eastern Pennsylvania!

(D) www.hikethePokes.org

This hiking club has a full calendar of hikes designed to discover the secrets of the Pocono Mountains and the surrounding area.

(E) www.howrocksareformed.org

Find general information and lots of examples about the formation of many types of rocks that are found in the eastern United States.

(F) www.geologyofPA.gov

Researchers from the U.S. Department of the Interior have collected the geologic records for the rock formation of every major mountain range in the United States.

**41** A student is writing a report on women's soccer. She wants to focus on the Women's World Cup games. She finds a source. Read the source and answer the question that follows.

> The Women's World Cup games are organized by the Fédération Internationale de Football Association, or FIFA. The World Cup is a championship soccer tournament. It is played every four years. Twenty-four teams from around the world play in the most competitive tournament in the most important international competition.

Which link from the menu on a web page would **most likely** help the student locate information about the players on the team from China?

Ⓐ Mission of FIFA

Ⓑ International Teams

Ⓒ World Cup Match Schedules

Ⓓ Tickets for the Women's World Cup

**42** A student is writing a research report on clowns. Here is a source that she is reading for her report. Read the source and answer the question that follows.

> Clowns date back hundreds of years. In ancient Rome, clowns were bald headed. They wore suits with extra padding to make them look jolly and funny. The most classic type of clown is called a white-face clown. A white-face clown uses white grease paint on his face. He paints red lips and a big smile so that people far away from the stage can see what he's doing. One of the most famous white-face clowns was called Grock. He made audiences laugh by doing tricks with chairs and stools.

The student has listed these main ideas. Which **two** main ideas will be supported by the information in this source?

Ⓐ Modern clowns

Ⓑ Major clown categories

Ⓒ Famous clowns in history

Ⓓ Getting a clown job with a circus

Ⓔ Training regimen for professional clowns

Ⓕ The day-to-day work of a circus clown

Name _____ Date _____

**43** For social studies class, a student will write a report about the animals of Madagascar. Read the paragraph from a science magazine. Underline **two** sentences from the paragraph that show evidence to support the main idea that many animals in Madagascar have developed unique adaptations to the island.

> Just off the coast of Africa is the island of Madagascar. It is host to hundreds of animal species that exist nowhere else in the world. Scientists believe that many species floated to the island from Africa. These animals evolved with little other animal competition. The lemur is one example of a uniquely adapted animal. Each lemur species has adapted to fill its own niche in the ecosystem. For example, the ring-tailed lemur spends most of its time on the ground foraging for fruit. The aye-aye is a lemur that eats insects that live under tree bark.

**44** A student is making a plan to research this question: How are video games marketed to children? The student finds the following paragraph in an article. Underline the sentence that **best** shows that this source has information the student can use.

> Video games can be addictive to children and adults. Many children spend so much time playing video games that they do not do all their homework. Studies have shown that playing video games can also affect how a student treats friends and family members. But video games are still sold for children to use. In fact, many video games are created with children in mind. There are video games based on popular television shows and movies. Video games often contain the same characters that children are familiar with from these shows.

# Performance Task 3
## Part 1

## Everglades National Park

**Task**

   Your class has been learning about the National Park System. You have been learning about many of the most popular parks. You become interested in learning more about Everglades National Park. You have found three sources about this topic in the school library.

   After you have reviewed these sources, you will answer some questions about them. Briefly scan the sources and the three questions that follow. Then, go back and read the sources carefully so you will have the information you will need to answer the questions and complete your research. You may use scratch paper to take notes on the information you find in the sources as you read.

   In Part 2, you will write an informational article using information you have read.

**Directions for Beginning**

   You will now review several sources. You can review any of the sources as often as you like.

**Research Questions**

   After reviewing the research sources, use the rest of the time in Part 1 to answer three questions about them. Your answers to these questions will be scored. Also, your answers will help you think about the information you have read, which should help you write your informational article.

   You may refer back to your scratch paper to review your notes when you think it would be helpful. Answer the questions in the spaces below the items.

   Your written notes on scratch paper will be available to you in Part 1 and Part 2 of the performance task.

Source #1

You have found an article that describes the role one animal plays in the ecosystem of the Everglades. (An ecosystem includes all of the animals and plants in a certain place, including how they interact.)

# Alligators and the Everglades

The Florida Everglades is an enormous wetland that is home to many creatures. They depend on the wetland for water, food, and shelter. Water has always been the key to life in the Everglades.

The climate in the Everglades alternates between flood and drought. Sixty inches of rain can fall in the rainy season. At the start of each winter dry season, the Everglades begins to dry up. What happens to the numerous creatures that make the Everglades their home? It might come as a surprise, but one animal helps the Everglades' wildlife survive when water becomes scarce. That animal is the American alligator. The American alligator lives throughout the southeastern United States, including southern Florida. That is where the Everglades is located. Male American alligators sometimes grow to be 15 feet long. Females are several feet shorter. Their color varies and may include olive green, brown, gray, or almost black.

Alligators have a huge impact on the Everglades and its other inhabitants. For example, several kinds of turtles use alligator nests to incubate their eggs. After the alligator has left the nest, the turtles will lay their eggs in them. Alligators also provide other wildlife with a necessary source of water during dry periods of the year. They use their feet, snouts, and tails to dig deep holes. These "gator holes" become small ponds that retain water. During the dry season, these holes are among the few places where standing water remains.

American alligator

As the Everglades dries out, many creatures retreat to gator holes. The holes become home to a variety of insects, turtles, fish, and wading birds. There, they can survive the dry times. When the rainy season returns, the animals spread out again. In this way, alligators benefit the Everglades by keeping other kinds of wildlife alive.

**122**

An alligator's diet includes fish, turtles, birds, snakes, and small animals. You might think alligator holes could be dangerous spots for these other animals. Sometimes they are. Mostly, the alligator conserves its energy during the dry season. It moves very little and lives off its own fat. It tends to ignore its new neighbors. The other animals live off the smaller fish, insects, and plants that live in the gator holes.

**Source #2**
You have found an article about the way another animal deals with the wet and dry seasons in the Everglades.

# Egrets in the Everglades

When we think of climate, we usually think of the four seasons. But in some places where the temperature doesn't vary that much, there may be only a wet season and a dry season. The Florida Everglades is such an environment. The wet season lasts from May to November. Temperatures at that time can reach an average of 90 degrees Fahrenheit, and the humidity can be over 90 percent. Afternoon thunderstorms can be expected daily. Heavy rainfalls typically subside quickly.

The summer rains keep the Everglades healthy. They also affect the habitat of wading birds like the great egret. As the water level rises, the birds find drier places. But every November the rains cease. Then, thousands of great egrets return to the Everglades. There they feast on the fish and other creatures that become easy prey in the drying marshes. In this way, the egret keeps the number of fish under control.

The great egret is one of the largest wading birds in the Everglades. Standing three feet tall, it has a wingspan of more than four feet. The bird uses its long legs to walk through the marshes. There it looks for fish to spear with its long, yellow bill.

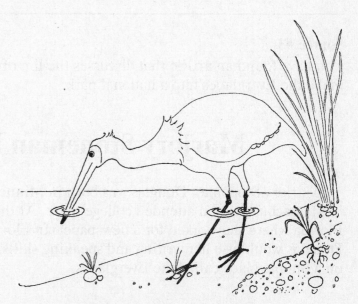

An egret uses its beak to catch fish to eat.

When the dry season begins, the marshes become less deep. The birds begin hunting at the shallowest places where fish become trapped. As the water level drops even more, the margin between wet and dry land shifts. Every day the birds fly to the new margins to find their food. Sometimes they use their feet to scrape along the marsh bottom until they stir up a fish. Then they snatch it up with their long beaks.

When the food supply becomes plentiful enough, the egrets build their nests. They make nests out of sticks, twigs, and stems. Although egrets prefer to fish alone, they nest in groups. These nesting areas are called rookeries.

The female lays two to five blue-green eggs. Both parents share three weeks of nest-sitting duties. Then comes the busiest time. When the chicks hatch, they are hungry. At first they are fed regurgitated fish. But as soon as the chicks are old enough, the parents hold whole fish over the nest for the young birds to grab. Sibling rivalry in the nest can become fierce. Feeding time is frantic for both parents and the young birds.

During the next six to seven weeks, the fledglings grow. During this time the parents fish in the deeper wetlands. The muddy hollows are called sloughs. With little water left, these sloughs can hold as many as 600 fish per square meter. Alligator holes also attract egrets. Built by alligators, these small ponds are a refuge for fish, frogs, and other creatures. These are all food for the egret. Young egrets grow stronger by eating this food, and soon they are ready to fly.

In the spring, the rains begin to flood the marshes again. Then the fish become hard to find. Once again it is time for most of the great egrets to fly northward out of the Everglades.

---

**Source #3**
You have found an article that discusses the life of a woman whose work helped make the Everglades into a national park.

# Marjory Stoneman Douglas

Marjory Stoneman Douglas was born in Minnesota in 1890. She grew up in Massachusetts and attended college there. At the age of 25, she moved to Florida where she worked for a newspaper. In Florida, Marjory Stoneman Douglas would use her writing and speaking skills to make a powerful impact on a unique place called the Everglades.

Name _____ Date _____

At the newspaper, Douglas wrote about the land, water, and wildlife of Florida. After leaving the newspaper, she wrote short stories, often about the Everglades. One story told how Florida's lovely egrets and other shorebirds were being killed off because people used their feathers to make fashionable hats.

The birds of the Everglades were threatened by hunting. A law to protect them had been passed in 1900, but hunters largely ignored it. In addition, developers were draining the marshes. They wanted to build on them. It wasn't possible to build houses on the marshy areas. They drained the water so that there was dry land. They ruined the area that many animals lived in. Marjory Stoneman Douglas joined with others to protect these wetlands forever. They wanted to create a national park.

After years of effort, Douglas and the other wetland supporters succeeded. In 1947, she was present when President Harry Truman dedicated Everglades National Park.

That same year, Douglas's book *The Everglades: River of Grass* was published. In this book, Douglas showed that the Everglades was not the worthless swampland that developers wanted to destroy. Douglas expressed her viewpoint in the opening sentences of her book. "There are no other Everglades in the world. They are, they always have been, one of the unique regions of the Earth, remote, never wholly known."

To Douglas, these wetlands were special. In the Everglades, a unique community of plants and animals depended on one another and on their watery home. Living and nonliving things that form connections are called an ecosystem. Douglas's book helped people understand the importance of protecting this ecosystem from human activities, its biggest threat.

Douglas influenced lawmakers and changed people's minds. She lived to be 108 years old. She had devoted most of her long life to conservation, especially of Florida wildlife. This remarkable woman made a difference in the world.

Name _____ Date _____

**1** Each source discusses how animals or people can affect a certain ecosystem. Give one detail from each source that describes how either animals or people affect the ecosystem of the Everglades.

_____

_____

_____

_____

_____

**2** Which source would **most likely** be the most helpful in understanding the process that leads to a place becoming a national park? Explain why this source is **most likely** the most helpful. Use **two** details from the source to support your explanation.

_____

_____

_____

_____

_____

**3** Using information from both Source #1 and Source #2, mark the boxes to show whether the events in the table below take place during the Everglades' dry season or wet season.

|  | **Dry Season** | **Wet Season** |
|---|---|---|
| Gator holes become a source of food, water, and homes for other animals. |  |  |
| Marshes become less deep. |  |  |
| Egrets fly northward, out of the Everglades. |  |  |
| Alligators move very little and live off their own fat to save energy. |  |  |
| Animals spread out into more areas of the Everglades. |  |  |
| Egrets build their nests. |  |  |

Name _____ Date _____

# Part 2

You will now review your notes and sources, and plan, draft, revise, and edit your writing. You may use your notes and go back to the sources. Now read your assignment and the information about how your writing will be scored, then begin your work.

**Your Assignment:**

Your teacher wants each student to write an informational article about one of the parks in the National Park System. You decide to write about Everglades National Park. The articles will be displayed at your school's upcoming Project Night to be read by other students, teachers, and parents.

Using more than one source, develop a main idea about Everglades National Park. Choose the most important information from more than one source to support your main idea. Then, write an informational article about your main idea that is several paragraphs long. Clearly organize your article and support your main idea with details from the sources. Use your own words except when quoting directly from the sources. Be sure to give the source title or number when using details from the sources.

**REMEMBER: A well-written informational article**

- has a clear main idea.
- is well-organized and stays on the topic.
- has an introduction and conclusion.
- uses transitions.
- uses details from the sources to support your main idea.
- puts the information from the sources in your own words, except when using direct quotations from the sources.
- gives the title or number of the source for the details or facts you included.
- develops ideas clearly.
- uses clear language.
- follows rules of writing (spelling, punctuation, and grammar usage).

Now begin work on your informational article. Manage your time carefully so that you can

1. plan your informational article.
2. write your informational article.
3. revise and edit the final draft of your informational article.

For Part 2, you are being asked to write an informational article that is several paragraphs long. Write your response in the space provided.

**127**

Name _____ Date _____

Remember to check your notes and your prewriting and planning as you write. Then, revise and edit your informational article.

_____

_____

_____

_____

_____

_____

_____

_____

_____

_____

_____

_____

_____

_____

_____

_____

_____

_____

_____

_____

_____

_____

_____

_____

_____

Name _____ Date _____

_____

_____

_____

_____

_____

_____

_____

_____

_____

_____

_____

_____

_____

_____

_____

_____

_____

_____

_____

_____

_____

_____

_____

_____

Name _____ Date _____

_____

_____

_____

_____

_____

_____

_____

_____

_____

_____

_____

_____

_____

_____

_____

_____

_____

_____

_____

_____

_____

_____

_____

_____

_____

_____

_____